Politics in Science

BASIC STUDIES IN POLITICS

Under the Editorship of

SHELDON S. WOLIN

University of California, Santa Cruz

MARLAN BLISSETT

The Lyndon B. Johnson School of Public Affairs
The University of Texas, Austin

Politics in Science

LITTLE, BROWN AND COMPANY *Boston*

ACKNOWLEDGMENTS

The following authors and publishers have granted permission to include
material from their publications. Specific pages are noted in the text.

Robert Bernhard: "Skeleton in the Closet of Physics: Whatever Became
of Reality," *Scientific Research*, Vol. 3, February 5, 1968.

David Bohm: Reprinted by permission, from David Bohm, *The Special
Theory of Relativity*, copyright 1965, W. A. Benjamin, Inc., Menlo Park,
California.

Daniel S. Greenberg: From *The Politics of Pure Science*. Copyright © 1967 by Daniel S. Greenberg. Reprinted by arrangement with the New American Library, Inc., New York.

Warren O. Hagstrom: *The Scientific Community*, Basic Books, Inc., Publishers, New York, 1965.

Thomas Kuhn: *The Structure of Scientific Revolutions* (Chicago: The University of Chicago Press, 1962). © The University of Chicago Press.

Michael Oakeshott: *Rationalism in Politics and Other Essays* (New York: Basic Books, Inc., 1962; London: Methuen & Co. Ltd.).

Michael Polanyi: "Growth of Science in Society," *Minerva*, Vol. 5, Summer 1967. *The Logic of Liberty* (Chicago: The University of Chicago Press, 1951; London: Routledge and Kegan Paul). © The University of Chicago Press. *Science, Faith and Society* (Chicago: The University of Chicago Press, 1964). © The University of Chicago Press.

Don K. Price: Reprinted by permission of the publisher from Don K. Price, *The Scientific Estate*, Cambridge, Mass.: The Belknap Press of Harvard University Press, Copyright, 1965, by the President and Fellows of Harvard College.

Marshall Walker: *The Nature of Scientific Thought*, © 1963, p. 78. Reprinted by permission of Prentice-Hall, Inc., Englewood Cliffs, N.J.

Alvin M. Weinberg: Reprinted from *Reflections on Big Science* by Alvin M. Weinberg by permission of the MIT Press, Cambridge, Massachusetts. © 1967 by Massachusetts Institute of Technology.

Sheldon S. Wolin: *Politics and Vision*, by permission of the author and Little, Brown and Company. Copyright © 1960 by Little, Brown and Company, Inc.

John Ziman: *Public Knowledge* (New York and London: Cambridge University Press, 1968).

Harriet Zuckerman: "The Sociology of the Nobel Prizes," *Scientific American*, Vol. 217, November 1967. Copyright © 1967 by Scientific American, Inc. All rights reserved.

To my mother and father

Foreword

Lᴵᴷᴇ ꜱᴏ ᴍᴀɴʏ areas of human knowledge to-
day, the study of politics and political institutions is undergoing
significant changes. A quarter-century ago only a few voices
challenged the prevailing consensus regarding the methods of
political science, the choice of problems, and the relative weight
assigned to the "factors" shaping political events, actions, and
behavior. Since then a revolution of uncertain proportions has
occurred, one that has been variously described as "the behavioral
movement" or "social science." It has visibly altered the climate
of political science and it has deeply affected the outlook of the
political scientist. No longer does he believe that political science
is a self-contained field. It has become second nature for him to
utilize methods, concepts, and data drawn from a wide range of
academic disciplines, such as sociology, psychology, and economics.

A marked self-consciousness about methods of inquiry characterizes much of the contemporary literature, whereas thirty years
ago only a few political scientists were troubled by this concern.
Today's political scientist is receptive to quantitative techniques,
eager to emphasize measurement, prepared to devise complex

classifications of empirical data, ready to experiment with abstract models, and engrossed with the intricacies of preparing questionnaires and organizing surveys of public opinion. These changes in method have also affected the outlook and the language of political science. Where his predecessors talked of "comparative government," he is apt to talk of "comparative political systems"; where they referred to "the process of government," he prefers to examine "the theory of decision making"; and where they spoke simply of "political theory," he will, more often than not, insist on a distinction between "normative theory" and "empirical theory" and, depending on his candor or concerns, will assert that his main interest lies with the latter. It is perhaps inevitable that a moderate reaction should set in and that questions should be raised among political scientists about whether they have not gone too far and too fast. There is an uneasiness that some settled issues ought to be reopened; that important features of politics have been ignored; that questions of choice and value have to be restored to a central position; and that the wonder of politics has been lost amidst the preoccupation with abstractions, graphs, and mathematical tables.

In the light of these changes and uncertainties there is good reason for political scientists and political theorists to reflect on the changing nature of their field of study and to report to a less specialized, but no less interested, audience how political events, practices, and behavior appear to the contemporary political scientist; what way or ways of looking at these matters he has found most useful and fruitful; and what problems he considers to be genuine and important.

This series of books was designed for such a purpose. The authors do not attempt to provide simply a digest of relevant facts, but to offer reflections and systematic analyses of the more significant and interesting areas of political science and political theory. Some concentrate upon familiar topics, such as federalism and political parties, but they seek to suggest the theoretically interesting problems raised by these traditional themes. Other studies, such as those dealing with political theory and ideology, proceed on a more theoretical plane, but with the explicit intention of indicating their relevance to the empirical concerns of political science. The standard set for this volume by Professor Blissett and for all the others is, I hope, within the best tradition of political science: the standard of reflective inquiry and informed analysis.

Three centuries ago Thomas Hobbes wrote that "the doctrine of right and wrong is perpetually disputed: whereas the doctrine of lines and figures is not so." By "lines and figures" Hobbes had in mind not only geometry but also early modern physics; the lack of controversy in these subjects was attributable, he thought, to the fact that "what be truth" was "a thing that crosses no man's ambition, profit or lust." Considering the extraordinary growth of science, a modern Hobbes might be prompted to say that modern science has been protected from public criticism and passions primarily because it has satisfied, rather than crossed, "man's ambition, profit or lust." During the past three centuries Western societies have steadily increased the level of public support for science until, in the twentieth century, it has reached spectacular heights. In return, science has furnished knowledge that, when integrated with industry and technology, has vastly increased the power of these societies: power to create and alter, to heal and protect, to control and liberate, to destroy and maim.

This exchange between science and society has created a mutual dependency which is nowhere more strikingly evident than in contemporary America. The survival of "Big Science," with its large-scale organizations, costly installations, big budgets, and numerous personnel, depends upon political support. In turn, American society has looked mainly to science to assure military security and insure domestic tranquility. To the extent that American society and other Western and non-Western societies are committed to the values of "progress," "development," or "modernization," they rely on science to provide a continual stimulus for innovative advances, as well as objective proof or assurance that such advances will occur. So weighty and universal is the influence of science in combination with industry and technology that contemporary societies, either in fact or in aspiration, are better described as scientific-technological-organizational, rather than by anachronistic labels such as "liberal-democratic," "social-democratic," or "Communistic."

After almost three centuries of unquestioning support of science, a growing disquietude is in evidence, especially in the United States. The benefits of scientific advances are seen in a more equivocal light, at least in some quarters. Widespread concern over the destruction of the natural environment, the depletion of resources, and the deterioration of the cities has raised questions about the responsibility of scientists for helping to promote innovation without paying commensurate attention to its consequences. Above all, spreading opposition to the Vietnam War revived questions about the political responsibility of scientists that had first been raised after the nuclear attack of Hiroshima and then allowed to lapse. As scientists became familiar public advocates, arguing and testifying about disarmament, the relative merits of missile systems, the advantages of moon-flights, and the urgent need for additional nuclear power plants, it was plain that scientists had become a powerful political force in determining the fate of the society and that the authority of scientific knowledge was being used to promote or oppose a particular ideology of political, military, and economic expansionism. The innocent belief that scientists can be counted on for detached and disinterested advice has been destroyed.

The most searching questions about modern science have been raised by writers who are strongly sympathetic to the aims and methods of science. Philosophers, historians, and scientists, such as Duhem, Burtt, Kuhn, Polanyi, Hanson, and Toulmin, have succeeded in raising questions that have made the claims and achievements of science seem tenuous. Thus the use of facts in formulating and validating theories no longer appears as a straightforward matter, but involves some arbitrariness and subjectivity. Likewise, considerable controversy surrounds the criteria that govern inquiry and testing. Persuasive arguments have been made that the criteria do not provide a neutral test for deciding between competing theories but only between theories that share the same assumptions. Finally, several writers have tried to show that many unscientific elements help decide why scientists surrender an established theory for a new one: elements that are more properly described as metaphysical, normative, intuitive, or aesthetic, rather than scientific or objective.

This intellectual ferment has raised questions about the influences affecting scientific perceptions and choices. From here it is but a short step to inquire into the sociological and political influences that enter into scientific judgments. The present volume by Marlan Blissett deals with some main questions about the "politics" of organized science. It has the virtue of bringing together the two considerations discussed previously, the political involvement of scientists and the cognitive problems of their research as affected by social and political factors as well as by personal ambitions and vested interests. His discussion of "consensual norms" reveals how powerfully research is affected by forces external to science, and his analysis of scientific organization is a perceptive account of the anxious efforts of scientists to cope with the increasingly fragmented and abstract nature of scientific knowledge. The reader will also be intrigued by the questionnaire used in this study; it presents vividly the competitive and insecure world of the individual scientist.

Professor Blissett's book is distinguished throughout by its judiciousness and fairmindedness. Today it is tempting to blame science for all of society's ills, perhaps because, as a society, we placed so much faith in science's redemptive possibilities. Tomorrow we shall have to define our collective fate in the consciousness that the blessings of science are mixed, and its philosophical status problematic.

Sheldon S. Wolin

Preface

THIS BOOK EXAMINES an issue that is both complex and controversial: the role of politics in science. The unifying theme is that "hidden systems" of influence and persuasion actively shape scientific perception but vary in relation to institutional configurations of power. In suggesting that science is considerably more than an analytical enterprise, my purpose is not to denigrate science, but to show that creative research involves the systematic generation and resolution of conflict.

Throughout the preparation of the study, I have benefited from the advice and criticism of many scholars, teachers, and students of political life. Although they are likely to deny it, whatever merit this undertaking may have is due to their assistance and concern.

A special debt of gratitude is owed to Professor Emmette S. Redford of the University of Texas at Austin; without his insistence and support, this work would never have been completed. Both his knowledge of organizations and critical attention to detail helped strengthen arguments and eliminate unnecessary complexities. Professor William S. Livingston, also of the University of Texas, generously consented to read the entire manuscript, patiently clarified many obscure passages, and improved its style; I am deeply grateful for his contribution.

Michael A. Weinstein and Richard L. Haines of Purdue University and Don E. Kash and Irvin L. (Jack) White, Director and Associate Director of the Science and Public Policy Program at the University of Oklahoma, listened carefully to my arguments, criticized them frankly, and offered valuable suggestions. Comments from David V. Edwards and Gideon Sjoberg of the University of Texas at Austin and from Alexander L. Clark, Associate Dean of the Lyndon B. Johnson School of Public Affairs, prevented several errors of fact and judgment.

My friend and former colleague John Reuss gave me the benefit of his discriminating intelligence and his extensive knowledge of science and public policy. His criticisms were especially useful during the final stages of research. My graduate assistants — Eileen Kaplan, Joanne Barszewski, Olivia Serio, and William Korte — cheerfully carried out many tedious assignments, pointed out a number of weaknesses, and tried hard to make my arguments stronger. In like manner, Carol Westberg and Freda Alexander of Little, Brown and Company furnished invaluable advice and editorial assistance.

Above all, I am indebted to Professor Sheldon S. Wolin of the University of California, Santa Cruz. He read an early version of the manuscript, recommended revisions, and provided support during moments of intense frustration.

Finally, my wife Karen prepared a number of tables and diagrams and offered useful stylistic suggestions. I greatly appreciate her attention and interest.

Marlan Blissett

Table
of contents

xv

Politics in Science

I

Science as an
institution

OUR MAJOR PURPOSE in this work is to uncover
the political techniques the scientific community utilizes in focusing and coordinating its research. Although some look upon the
development of science as a "socially unproblematical process," [1]
this study is an effort to show that conflict generation and resolution, together with institutional norms of behavior, are extremely
important to scientific inquiry.

The political techniques that scientists use refer to strategies
for controlling or influencing decisions on what problems to investigate, the validity of research paradigms, the verification of
hypotheses, and the relation of science to the outside world. The
content of these decisions may vary from one discipline to another, but the process itself — the ordered competition among
individual scientists and research groups — is maintained throughout the scientific community.

Describing science in this way assumes an organizational set-

---

[1] Talcott Parsons, *Essays in Sociological Theory* (Glencoe, Ill.: The Free
Press, 1949), p. 34.

ting. Indeed, present scientific growth is unimaginable without institutional means for coordinating the dynamics of research and directing these activities against increasingly explicit problems. This development has been largely responsible for pushing "metaphysical" issues farther and farther from the center of scientific investigation and for focusing attention upon "well-defined, finite problems that appear to be soluble with the methods and evidence available." [2] In short, the organizational features of science both reflect and contribute to the rationalization of inquiry.

As a rationalized activity, science must be seen initially as a highly refined extension of the manipulative order-creating mechanism of the brain.[3] Its methodological emphasis upon a proper sequence of observation and experimentation is closely analogous to the cognitive response of higher mammals in coping with individual situations that are inherently complex (such as hunting or building).[4] But the distinctive quality that separates science from simpler forms of cognition is its collective utilization of singular skills. As J. D. Bernal has argued, science can no longer be thought of as an expression of individual cognition or expertise; it is rather a social achievement built upon cooperative effort and sustained by explicit features of coordination.[5]

Perhaps the most obvious means of coordinating the collective activity of science is through language.[6] But as the organization of science increases in specialization, its language becomes more and more removed from the concrete circumstances that originally gave it meaning and shape. Weinberg has explained this development as a response to the fragmenting tendency of specialized research. Thus, in order to maintain a high quality of communication within, as well as across, disciplines, science is forced to reintegrate itself at progressively higher levels of ab-

[2] Harvey Brooks, *The Government of Science* (Cambridge, Mass.: The M.I.T. Press, 1968), p. 208.

[3] J. D. Bernal, *Science in History* (New York: Hawthorn Books, 1965), p. 15.

[4] *Ibid.*

[5] *Ibid.*, p. 16.

[6] *Ibid.*

straction.[7] The result is an "increasingly abstract and insubstantial picture of the physical universe." [8]

An illustration lies in contrasting Bernal's description of the "simple ruggedness" of Rutherford's pioneering ideas on subatomic phenomena with a contemporary statement of the meaning of elementary particle research.

> Rutherford thought first of the atoms, then of the sub-atomic particles he had discovered, exactly as ordinary material particles: as projectiles, tennis, or billiard balls. He treated them as such and found out things about them from how they moved or bounced. Sometimes the particles did not behave as he expected. He accepted the new discovery as a fact and assimilated it by making a new imaginative picture of the structure with which he was dealing. Thus, step by step, he proceeded from the study of unstable atoms of radioactivity to the discovery of the atomic nucleus and the general theory of the atom.[9]

But today Harvey Brooks has urged:

> In physics the sharp distinction which used to be made between the object and its relations to other objects has been replaced by the idea that the object (or elementary particle) is nothing but the nexus of the various relations in which it participates. In physics . . . form has tended to achieve a status higher than substance.[10]

The creation and use of higher order abstractions, however, is not the final means of coordinating the vast expanse of scientific research. Mechanisms exist within the scientific community for certifying the validity of abstractions that cannot be compared against the concrete experience of nature. (In the more advanced empirical sciences, traces of nature are almost altogether "lost.") By an intricate political process the "form" of scientific concepts is reliably certified and the whole organization of science is converted into a massive perceptual tool. This is an achievement of

---

[7] Alvin Weinberg, *Reflections on Big Science* (Cambridge, Mass.: The M.I.T. Press, 1966), p. 44.

[8] Brooks, *The Government of Science*, p. 213.

[9] Bernal, *Science in History*, p. 537.

[10] Brooks, *The Government of Science*, p. 213.

subtle nuance and great complexity, but it emphasizes perhaps the most important development within science since the discovery of the rational experiment. Briefly expressed, the politics of science serves to mobilize, coordinate, and certify the diverse activities of research. It is characterized by techniques of influence and persuasion that select and "enforce" consensual patterns of perception and build from them convincing models of the external world.

Defining the politics of science in these terms reduces the whole process to an instrumental function. Indeed, this is precisely what is intended. The politics of science is not an architectonic activity, but a mechanism for achieving the institutional goals of science and for monitoring the viability of its collective decisions. Although this function is crucial, the specific pattern it assumes depends upon the type of institutional setting within which scientific work is done.

The most conventional assumption, and one explored in this study, is that science operates within a professional framework. At this level its most distinctive characteristic, aside from maintaining a tradition of inquiry and accompanying research techniques, is the autonomous relation assumed toward other social institutions. Norman Storer has argued that the autonomous requirements of science extend only to recruiting, training, and controlling professional membership.[11] But he also suggests that for the profession to survive, it must evolve stable relations with larger society — contacts convincing enough to bring in material support. Herein, of course, lies the paradox of the autonomous system: it does not provide a recognized service to the community (as does medicine or law), yet it continually solicits economic assistance from the institutions of larger society.

The tensions produced by this interaction are integral to the professionalizing tendency in American science. As George H. Daniels has shown, the entire process is a step-by-step encroachment upon commonly held assumptions and skills — in which

[11] Norman Storer, *The Social System of Science* (New York: Holt, Rinehart & Winston, 1966), pp. 17-19.

an activity customarily discharged by a nonexclusive group or by everyone is appropriated as the exclusive possession of a professional group.[12] Although this is a complicated development, the coveted route to autonomy involves at least three identifiable stages: preemption of task, institutionalization of function, and legitimation of purpose.[13]

The organizational characteristics of science begin to appear during institutionalization — when social structures are developed "for regularizing relationships among colleagues and between colleagues and outsiders." [14] This period is made especially turbulent by conflicts that arise over the creation of formal associations having publication responsibilities and the search for more stable relations with larger society. Once the organization of science has been established, its survival depends upon how well it can convince the outside community of its importance. As Daniels says:

> The frankly avowed pursuit of *pure* knowledge is a luxury that a democratic society will allow only the well-established profession. This implies that in the early stages it will be hazardous to attempt to justify scientific training and research in terms of scientific values alone. Until such time that the power of science over the environment becomes perfectly obvious, the scientist must seek some other means of contact with the relevant public. That is to say, the emergent profession has no choice but to justify its work in terms of its social purposes, and in doing so, it must appeal to general cultural values.[15]

The justification that American science has made for its claim to autonomy is curious. On the one hand it appeals to the prospects of gaining greater and more reliable knowledge of the natural world — by the open participation of all qualified parties; but on the other, it seeks to fulfill the requirements or "needs"

[12] George H. Daniels, "The Process of Professionalization in American Science: The Emergent Period, 1820 to 1860," *Isis* 58, no. 2 (Summer 1967): 152.

[13] *Ibid.*, p. 152.

[14] *Ibid.*, p. 156.

[15] *Ibid.*, p. 160.

of the nation-state. Although sometimes overlooked, this last theme has been present from the earliest stages of professionalized science in the United States. In 1851, the president of the newly formed American Association for the Advancement of Science could say:

> Our country asks for other things from us. . . . And men of science of this day, as in times past, labor for progress. We will hope to have "American methods" in the other branches of science, besides practical astronomy.
>
> If these associations [professional associations] have proved themselves of value in other countries . . . there is none where they could have promised to be so important to the interests of national science as in the United States. Organization here, for good or for evil, is the means to the end. While science is without organization it is without power.[16]

Whatever the outcome of this development, the future of the autonomous system is likely to depend upon events beyond its control — upon political and economic forces that, in combination, have the power to change the whole form of scientific organization. One important manifestation of this trend is the extent to which the pressures of society have already been felt within the distinguished university — long recognized as the protective shield of the independent activities of science. Clark Kerr has convincingly shown that

> the campus and society are undergoing a somewhat reluctant and cautious merger, already well advanced. M.I.T. is at least as much related to industry and government as Iowa State ever was to agriculture. Extension work is really becoming "life-long learning." Harvard today has four post graduate doctors in its medical school for every one still working for his degree; so also for many other skills including business. Television makes it possible for extension to reach into literally every home; the boundaries of the university are stretched to embrace all of society. The student becomes alumnus and the alumnus continues

---

[16] Address of A. D. Bache, President of the AAAS, 1851. *Proceedings,* American Association for the Advancement of Science (New York: G. P. Putnam, 1852), p. lii.

as student; the graduate enters the outside world and the public enters the classroom and the laboratory.[17]

If Kerr's analysis is correct, the transformation of the university may portend new forms of scientific organization. But these are not yet visible and what they may mean for the deployment of scientific expertise is not yet clear. Moreover, the political techniques that may eventually evolve to coordinate the activities of science within these new forms are still highly problematic.

In this study we anticipate these developments by pulling together a number of arguments about the prospective relations of science. But most of the analysis is focused upon the professional characteristics of the autonomous system and the political and social factors that regulate its perceptual capacity.

Chapter 2 is an effort to conceptualize the "spatial" problems in present and prospective scientific behavior. Four models of "scientific space" are explained: science as an autonomous profession; science as an organization for applied missions; science as an "estate of the realm"; and science as a tertiary industry. In Chapter 3, the social parameters of professionalized science are refocused by exploring the structure of scientific research and the social norms that define its role expectations. Our argument here is that structural support for the autonomous system is substantially provided by university departments, but that research specialization tends to prevent the development of a sense of unity. Moreover, the argument continues, research norms are important to the strategy of political manipulation and control, for they help stabilize the behavior expectations of scientific research. Yet, not all norms are clearly affirmed, and those which are rejected or which are held ambiguously pose problems in maintaining the spatial integrity of the autonomous system.

Chapter 4 represents an attempt to examine the intricate pattern of politics within autonomous research, specifically: (1) the consensual nature of scientific inquiry and the power configurations that attend it, (2) the emergence and resolution of scientific

[17] Clark Kerr, *The Uses of the University* (Cambridge, Mass.: Harvard University Press, 1963), p. 115.

disputes, and (3) efforts to justify the activities of science to the larger community. In the concluding chapter, future pressures against the organization of professionalized science by governmental, military, and economic institutions are anticipated. This chapter is built around the possibility that the spatial characteristics of science may be deeply influenced by power configurations in the broader society. Thus, although the internal politics of the profession refines and focuses the perceptual reliability of research, the external politics of power is primarily responsible for establishing the institutional scope of scientific work. By examining three overlapping profiles of power concentration — the liberal state, the bureaucratic state, and the postindustrial state — we try to link the models of science developed in Chapter 2 to larger complexes of political decision-making.

2

The spatial dimensions
of science

THE MOST IMPORTANT FUNCTION of professional-
ized science is to create, discover, and disseminate valid perceptions of nature.[1] In discharging this activity, scientific disciplines
respond to both physical and social stimuli, the former being
measured largely by artificial instrumentation and the latter by
widening circles of individual and collegial judgment.

Interpretations of the relation between physical and social
factors in perception have given rise to two prevailing explanations, both relevant to scientific inquiry. The first insists that
physical signals from nature create within the brain a matching
correspondence between the structure of the percept and the
physical variables of the stimuli.[2] The second holds that the substance of the percept is not defined by the physical properties of

[1] For an excellent discussion of science as a perception system see the
appendix essay, "Physics and Perception," in David Bohm, *The Special
Theory of Relativity* (New York: W. A. Benjamin, 1965), pp. 185–230.

[2] James J. Gibson, "The Concept of Stimulus in Psychology," *The American Psychologist* 15, no. 9 (September 1960):695.

external stimuli, but grows out of a constitutive act from within the individual.[3]

Both perspectives deal with individual acts of perception, not with collective or social systems. Yet the research focus of science, though sensitive to individual perception, is fundamentally composed of several proximate, or partially overlapping, systems of collective cognition. Precisely this feature makes the institutional characteristics of scientific inquiry an important determinant of research. For at increasingly abstract levels of scientific investigation, patterns of political and social "stimuli" predominantly influence what is "seen." Hence, institutional relations form areas of "social space" that affect science by changing the previous understanding within which new perceptions are received. In this respect, areas of social space serve much the same function in science as do instrumental paraphernalia (such as the microscope or telescope), for they create and expose different domains of experience.

As described here, social space consists of the structural features of scientific activity — how scientists and scientific institutions interact, not just with each other, but with institutions of larger society as well. Each level of social space sustains patterns of politics that require individual and institutional adjustments, some of which are *adaptive* (that is, they make no overt demands for particular responses), and others *manipulated* (involving active attempts to bring about desired behavior). In this last group the "politics" of science is most starkly visible, although both types are part of "pressure patterns" existing within all scientific activity.

The structural complexity of modern society has enormously increased the social space in which science functions. But in the absence of geographical features to identify it, the characteristics of this space must be affirmed through argument. In this chapter four arguments about the social space of science are presented. The first suggests that science is an autonomous profession — oriented toward the pursuit of basic research and largely insulated from the demands and pressures of larger society. The second

---

[3] M. D. Vernon, *A Further Study of Visual Perception* (Cambridge: Cambridge University Press, 1952), p. 47.

urges that science is an organized attack against shortages in physical energy and against the increasing semantic confusion produced by professional research activity. Although these goals are expensive to achieve, they are nevertheless considered essential for the development of applied science and technology. The third argument "visualizes" science as an "estate of the realm" with enough potential influence to affect the relative balances of constitutional power. The last describes the social space of science as the equivalent of a tertiary industry — one whose operations are completely integrated into the purposive structures of society.

Each argument stresses different aspects of "scientific space." We will see what they are and how they relate to one another in this chapter.

SCIENCE AS AN AUTONOMOUS PROFESSION

One of the most carefully preserved simplifications of scientific culture is the belief that the activities of science bear a structural resemblance to economic laissez-faire. If this perspective is sound, contemporary science can be viewed as an organizational atavism with eighteenth-century characteristics. Its struggle to preserve its autonomy — that is, to maintain a distinctive structural identity — places science in competition with organizations such as the state, industry, and other knowledge disciplines, that wish either to reduce its scope or to co-opt its skills for social redeployment.

No scientist has felt the pull of external influences upon science more strongly than Michael Polanyi, and no one has confronted the problem more intensely. Polanyi's appeal (which is both normative and descriptive) emphasizes the importance to science of a self-coordinated system of independent initiatives that sustains and regulates high professional standards. Such organization, he argues, is the only reliable means of uncovering new knowledge and advancing science equally on all fronts. In words and metaphors reminiscent of Adam Smith he suggests that

> self-coordination of independent initiatives leads to a joint result which is unpremeditated by any of those who bring it about. Their coordination is guided as by "an invisible hand" towards

the joint discovery of a hidden system of things. Since its end-result is unknown, this kind of cooperation can only advance in stages, and the total performance will be the best possible if each consecutive step is decided upon by someone most competent to do so. We may imagine this condition to be fulfilled for the fitting together of a jig-saw puzzle if each helper watches out for any new opportunities arising along a particular section of the so far completed patch of the puzzle, and also keeps an eye on a particular lot of pieces, so as to fit them in wherever a chance presents itself. . . . We may affirm that the pursuit of science by independent self-coordinated initiatives assures the most efficient possible organization of scientific progress. And we may add, again, that any authority which would undertake to direct the work of the scientist centrally, would bring the progress of science virtually to a standstill.[4]

Lending support to Polanyi's concept of self-coordination in science is Lord Brain, former president of the British Association for the Advancement of Science. Although he emphasizes the individualist aspects of scientific pursuits, the implication is quite clear that the result is a collective contribution to an impersonal system of scientific knowledge.

Scientists . . . meet one another to exchange ideas, to promote their own particular branch of science, or science in general, or because they are aware of its social implications. Nevertheless, such collective activities, important though they may be in them-selves, play a small part in their lives. Scientists, though they must always be aware of the work of their fellows in their own fields, are essentially individualists; and the body of knowledge to which they are contributing is an impersonal one. Apart from contributing to it, they have no collective consciousness, inter-est, or aim.[5]

Both Polanyi and Brain want to stress the lack of importance to science of any centrally directed effort at total coordination. But

[4] Michael Polanyi, *The Republic of Science: Its Political and Economic Theory* (Chicago: Roosevelt University, 1962), pp. 7–8.

[5] *Science* 148 (April 9, 1965): 192–198, quoted in Gordon Tullock, *The Organization of Inquiry* (Durham, N.C.: Duke University Press, 1966), pp. 4–5.

Polanyi feels that much more is at stake. The whole structure of self-coordination, though both progressive and efficient, is nevertheless exposed, he argues, to economic and technological pressures that threaten it from all sides. When either or both of these forces are linked to the power of the state, the scientific activity involved is likely to atrophy and eventually die. Polanyi is not worried about hypothetical conditions or the possibilities of an Orwellian nightmare. He points with both fear and disappointment to the Lysenko invasion of cytogenetics in Russia during the 1930s.[6] This event temporarily paralyzed a promising line of research and directly challenged the authority of professionalized scientific opinion.

Polany recounts how Trofim D. Lysenko, an ingenious manipulator of agricultural technique, developed a new theory of heredity at variance with the scientifically accepted Mendelian view. Lysenko's theory rested upon the possibility of creating hereditary hybridization in plants by grafting — a position that directly contradicted the foundation of Mendel's laws of heredity and seriously questioned the work going on in cytogenetics. The Soviet government was deeply committed to the idea that, by altering man's external environment, it could shape not only his social institutions but the nature of man himself. Lysenko's scientific experiments seemed to confirm this possibility. That Lysenko's work was at odds with scientific opinion did not matter. Was not this opinion, after all, the product of bourgeois scientists? The Presidium thought so and began to criticize the Russian scientific community for failing to reconstruct itself. Moreover, it launched a massive program to "prove" that new life styles could be produced through a concentrated technical effort. Because Lysenko's experiments seemed to support this ideological end, the Communist Party ordered Soviet biologists to reconsider the significance of his work.

In Polanyi's judgment the direct intervention of the Communist Party had unfortunate consequences for Soviet biological science, for it denied the power of professional scientists to cer-

[6] Michael Polanyi, *The Logic of Liberty* (Chicago: University of Chicago Press, 1951), pp. 59–66.

tify biological theories through replication of experiments and collegial criticism.[7] Polanyi relates the event in the sad, sympathetic tones of an international scientist.

The ambitious and unscrupulous figures who rise to power on the tide of a movement against science, do not withdraw when

[7] For an excellent recent account of Stalin's "ethos of science" and the struggle against it see Alexander Vucinich, "Science and Morality: A Soviet Dilemma," *Science* 159, no. 15 (March 1968): 1208–1212. Vucinich indicates that "current writings on the professional problems of scientific work show the determined search of Soviet scholars for a genuine community of scientists which would protect the moral and intellectual interests of science." He goes on to observe that "Petr Kapitsa sums up the problem in the following statements: 'It is easy to see that the progress of science requires the existence of a fully developed scientific community. . . . The creation of a healthy and advanced community of scientists is an enormous task to which we give far too little attention. This task is more difficult than the training of selected young talent or the construction of large institutes. . . . *The community of scientists alone can objectively judge the achievements of science. . . . Only an advanced scientific community can fully appraise the intellectual power of a scientific discovery independently of its practical significance.*' " [emphasis mine] (p. 1210)

A most penetrating essay developed around the problem of curing virus diseases of the potato and one which highlights Lysenkoian themes is David Joravsky's "The Lysenko Affair," *Scientific American* 207, no. 5 (November 1962): 42–49. The author concludes his study in an exciting and provocative way:

In a time of great upheaval Lysenko created a crude, bullying, self-deceiving "agrobiology" to accord with a crude, bullying, self-deceiving agricultural policy. *Recently that policy and its partner in plant science have been fitfully disintegrating. It remains to be seen whether or not the necessities inherent in the modern agriculture that industrialized populations require will bring the full restoration of objectivity in economics and plant science, and along with that the restoration of full freedom of scientific discussion.* Perhaps this proposition should be restated on a comparative basis, for scientific objectivity and freedom of scientific discussion are not absolutes. It remains to be seen whether or not a government preaching communism and the collective spirit can manage farmers and scientists as efficiently as governments preaching enterprise and individualism. [emphasis mine] (p. 49)

Additional information concerning the relations between research biologists and Soviet politicians is available in Zhores A. Medvedev, *The Rise and Fall of T. D. Lysenko,* trans. by I. Michael Lerner (New York: Columbia University Press, 1969).

scientists make their last abject surrender. On the contrary, they stay to complete the triumph by directing against their yielding opponents the charge of insincerity. . . . The demonstration given here of the corruption of a branch of science, caused by placing its pursuit under the direction of the State, seems to me complete. Particularly, as there can be no doubt of the unwavering desire of the Soviet Government to advance the progress of science. It has spent large sums on laboratories, on equipment and on personnel. Yet these subsidies . . . benefited science only so long as they flowed into channels controlled by independent scientific opinion, whereas as soon as their allocation was accompanied by attempts at establishing governmental direction, they exercised a destructive influence.[8]

Professionalized scientific opinion must, Polanyi insists, operate within an organizational world free from exogenous influences — free from the demands of interest clusters that could dilute its impersonal ("systemic") standards of evaluation. Moreover, he contends that structural autonomy is the only means of preserving the five professional functions necessary for scientific growth, functions which guarantee to a self-coordinated community of scientists control over the basic processes of knowledge certification: [9]

1. The selection of papers for publication;
2. Conferring scientific honors and research funds;
3. Publication of textbooks and popularizations of science;
4. The teaching of science in universities and lower schools; and
5. The protection of the individual scientist in the pursuit of his own research work.

Once secure in these responsibilities, professionalized science is driven toward an "unanticipated rendezvous with truth" by the independent motivations of individual scientists.

The professional functions of science, however, represent only the "public" dimensions within which the work of scientific innovation and commitment to research paradigms occurs. The "private" or personal dimension makes up the intuitive reservoir

[8] Polanyi, *The Logic of Liberty*, pp. 65–66.
[9] *Ibid.*, p. 66.

that guides the scientist until he makes contact with reality. The genius of Polanyi's perspective is that it anticipates no fundamental conflict between the "tacit dimension" of individual discovery and the practices "providing for mutual reliance and mutual discipline among scientists." [10] The overlapping features of each dimension are governed by internalized and socially sanctioned rules developed during ordinary research activity. These rules, however, cannot be codified,[11] for they are endemic to the research process itself — and ultimately to the whole tradition of scientific inquiry.[12] The quality of cognitive expectation built

---

[10] Michael Polanyi, *Science, Faith and Society* (Chicago: University of Chicago Press, 1964), p. 47. Originally published by Geoffrey Cumberlege (London: Oxford University Press, 1946).

[11] *Ibid.*, p. 33.

[12] To suggest a further overlap between the dynamics of science and political inquiry, attention should be drawn to how closely Polanyi's concept of scientific organization parallels Michael Oakeshott's impression of human knowledge in general and political knowledge in particular. In a passage that supports his belief that true political knowledge is largely the product of "practice" or tradition, Oakeshott observes:

> Every science, every art, every practical activity requiring skill of any sort, indeed every human activity whatsoever, involves knowledge. And, universally, this knowledge is of two sorts, both of which are always involved in any actual activity. It is not, I think, making too much of it to call them two sorts of knowledge, because (though in fact they do not exist separately) there are certain important differences between them. The first sort of knowledge I will call technical knowledge or knowledge of technique. In every art and science, and in every practical activity, a technique is involved. In many activities this technical knowledge is formulated into rules which are, or may be, deliberately learned, remembered, and, as we say, put into practice; but whether or not it is, or has been, precisely formulated, its chief characteristic is that it is susceptible of precise formulation, although special skill and insight may be required to give it that formulation. The technique (or part of it) of driving a motor car on English roads is to be found in the Highway Code, the technique of cookery is contained in the cookery book, and the technique of discovery in natural science or in history is in their rules of research, of observation and verification. The second sort of knowledge I will call practical, because it exists only in use, is not reflective and (unlike technique) cannot be formulated in rules. This does not mean, however, that it is an esoteric sort of knowledge. It means only that the method by which it may be shared and becomes common knowledge is not the method of formulated doctrine. And if we consider it from this point of

by the intricate overlay of past scientific experience is too complex for linear (or technical) transmission. It cannot be satisfactorily written down or straightforwardly expressed in textbooks or research manuals. A "full initiation into the premises of science can [thus] be gained only by the few who possess the gifts for becoming independent scientists, and they usually achieve it only through close personal association with the intimate views and practice of a distinguished master." [13]

The master intuitively selects the "right" problems for further work; he senses the techniques that apply to his interests, responds inventively to new evidence, overcomes unanticipated difficulties, and regards his own interpretations with great flexibility and skill.[14] According to Polanyi the qualities of the master form an "essential vision," an insight that, glimpsed by the young apprentice, qualifies him to be a scientist.

> The morsels of science which he [the young apprentice] picks up — even though often dry or else speciously varnished — instill in him the intimation of intellectual treasures and creative joys far beyond his ken. His intuitive realization of a great system of valid thought and of an endless path of discovery sustain him in laboriously accumulating knowledge and urge him on to penetrate into intricate brain-racking theories. Sometimes he will also find a master whose work he admires and whose manner and outlook he accepts for his guidance. Thus his mind will become assimilated to the premises of science. *The scientific institution of reality henceforth shapes his perception. He learns the methods*

---

view, it would not, I think, be misleading to speak of it as traditional knowledge. In every activity this sort of knowledge is also involved; the mastery of any skill, the pursuit of any concrete activity is impossible without it. . . . Again, these two sorts of knowledge are involved in any genuinely scientific activity. The natural scientist will certainly make use of the rules of observation and verification that belong to his technique, but these rules remain only one of the components of his knowledge; advance in scientific discovery was never achieved merely by following the rules.

Rationalism in Politics and Other Essays (New York: Basic Books; London: Methuen & Co. Ltd., 1962), pp. 7–8.

[13] Polanyi, *Science, Faith and Society*, p. 43.

[14] *Ibid.*, pp. 43–44.

of scientific investigation and accepts the standards of scientific value.[15]

The master-pupil relation is a small part of the "wider set of institutions" that "publically" order scientific discoveries and that both encourage and develop the "premises of science." [16] These are the institutions carrying out the professional functions of science. Though essential to the order and maintenance of scientific knowledge, the institutions of professionalized science do not destroy the "sovereign" position of each scientist, for, as Polanyi suggests:

> There are differences in rank between scientists, but these are of secondary importance: everyone's position is sovereign. The Republic of Science realizes the ideal of Rousseau, of a community in which each is an equal partner in a General Will. But this identification makes the General Will appear in a new light. It is seen to differ from any other will by the fact that it cannot alter its own purpose. It is shared by the whole community because each member of it shares in a joint task.[17]

Each scientist is "sovereign," but authority is not equally dispersed.[18] Obviously, some scientists are more influential than others and play important leadership roles within the scientific community. Polanyi admits that "exceptional authority" exists, but he argues that it is not institutionally determined. Rather it depends upon the qualities of the individual scientist who "is granted exceptional influence by the fact that his opinion is valued and asked for." Moreover, this "self-government of science is largely unofficial; the decisions lie with scientific opinion at large, focused and expressed on each particular occasion by the most competent experts commanding wide confidence." [19]

Scientific leaders — men whose judgment is consistently sought — make up the functional links of a system of evaluation that covers all scientific inquiry. They are the opinion-makers and

[15] *Ibid.*, p. 44, emphasis mine.
[16] *Ibid.*, p. 47.
[17] *Ibid.*, pp. 16–17.
[18] *Ibid.*, p. 48.
[19] *Ibid.*

breakers of scientific thought, but their roles are informal and, as Polanyi implies, free from external *political* contamination:

> This coherence of valuations throughout the whole range of science underlies the unity of science. It means that any statement recognized as valid in one part of science can, in general, be considered as underwritten by all scientists. It also results in a general homogeneity of and a mutual respect between all kinds of scientists, by virtue of which science forms an organic unity.[20]

Professionalized science, as Polanyi has discussed it, bears a striking affinity to the social perspectives of Edmund Burke, Thomas Paine, and Adam Smith. Polanyi, in common with these writers, believes that any kind of overhead direction — either by selected members within the social system of science or by the state — can produce only harmful consequences. Comprehensive supervision critically disables spontaneous self-adjustment, which embodies all that is creative, ingenious, and industrious in man, and through which the impersonal opinion of collective judgment becomes the final arbiter of claims upon reality. Thus, within the community of sciences,

> both its liberties and its servitudes are determined by its striving for self-improvement, which in turn is determined by the intimations of truth yet to be revealed, calling on men to reveal them. This view transcends the conflict between Edmund Burke and Tom Paine. It rejects Paine's demand for the absolute self-determination of each generation, but does so for the sake of his own ideal of unlimited human and social improvement. It accepts Burke's thesis that freedom must be rooted in tradition, but transposes it into a system cultivating radical progress.[21]

The influence of Adam Smith on Polanyi is also much greater than his gift of metaphor, for the "invisible hand" (to which Polanyi alludes) characterizes neither the full impact of Smith's thought nor the implications it has for Polanyi's emphasis on professional evaluation. Polanyi's notion of the collective and impersonal character of scientific opinion (which controls the pro-

---

[20] *Ibid.*, p. 49.
[21] Polanyi, *The Republic of Science*, p. 26.

fessional standards of scientific achievement) finds structural support in Smith's *Theory of Moral Sentiments*, in which he confronts the problem of how men make moral judgments "first of their neighbors and afterwards of themselves." [22] Essentially this is accomplished by reifying the norms of the community in the form of an "impartial spectator" who serves as the superego of each individual psyche. The role that Smith outlines for the spectator unmistakably resembles what Polanyi calls the "professional conscience" of the scientific community. Compare these statements, the first by Smith and the second by Polanyi:

> No man during either the whole course of his life, or that of any considerable part of it, ever trod steadily and uniformly in the paths of prudence, of justice, or of proper beneficence, whose conduct was not principally directed by a regard to the sentiments of the supposed impartial spectator, of the great inmate of the breast, the great judge and arbiter of conduct. If in the course of the day we have swerved in any respect from the rules which he prescribes to us; . . . it is this inmate who, in the evening, calls us to an account for all those omissions and violations. . . .[23]

> It would thus appear that when the premises of science are held in common by the scientific community each must subscribe to them by an act of devotion. These premises form not merely a guide to intuition, but also a guide to conscience; they are not merely indicative, but also normative. . . . [Therefore] before claiming discovery [one] must listen to his scientific conscience. As he advances in life his professional conscience acquires a variety of new functions; in publishing papers, in criticizing those by other authors, in lecturing to students, in selecting candidates for appointments, in a hundred ways he has to form judgments that are ultimately guided by the ideal of science as interpreted by his conscience.[24]

---

[22] From the extended title: Adam Smith, *Theory of Moral Sentiments; or An Essay toward the Analysis of the Principles by Which Men Naturally Judge Concerning the Conduct and Character, First of Their Neighbors, and afterwards of Themselves*, 6th ed. (London: Strahan and Cadel, 1790), Vol. 2.

[23] *Ibid.*, pp. 187–188.

[24] Polanyi, *Science, Faith and Society*, pp. 54–55.

Moreover, for Polanyi, the impersonal force of scientific opinion serves as a "systemic signal" for the allocation of scarce epistemic resources to areas of professional specialization in which they are most needed. In this, too, he parallels Smith. "Scientific opinion" bears more than a superficial resemblance to Smith's concept of price, which works as an impersonal index of the supply and demand of the market.[25] In Polanyi, the "signal" given by scientific opinion may induce the movement of resources from areas where scientific demand has been satisfied to those where it continues.

"Demand," however, is a very complex category within Polanyi's system of spontaneous coordination. It reflects theoretical "need," which may vary considerably from discipline to discipline, as individual research adapts to problems "sustaining the most intense attention and effort of thought." [26] Essentially "demand" is regarded as necessary to raise the level of theoretical achievement in any area of science, and it is always sensitive to three factors: the "intrinsic interest of the subject matter," "the profundity or systematic interest of the generalizations involved," and "the certainty and precision of the new statements." [27] Thus:

> In every branch of science this threefold valuation will have to be applied jointly, due regard being given particularly to the wide variations in the intrinsic interest of different subject matters. Accordingly, less precision and systematic coherence will be required for example in the study of living matter and of human beings in particular, than in the study of inanimate bodies. The leaders of scientific opinion are responsible for maintaining all along the advancing frontier of science approximately uniform standards of value. Guided by these standards, they will keep shifting resources and encouragement to the more successful growing points of science, at the expense of the less fruitful

[25] Here is Smith's statement of the point: "The market price of every particular commodity is regulated by the proportion between the quantity which is actually brought to market and the demand of those who are willing to pay the natural price of the commodity, or the whole value of the rent, labor, and profit which must be paid in order to bring it thither." Adam Smith, *The Wealth of Nations: Representative Sections*, Bruce Mazlish, ed. (New York: Bobbs-Merrill, 1961), Book I, pp. 53–54.

[26] Polanyi, *Republic of Science*, p. 10.

[27] Polanyi, *Logic of Liberty*, p. 55.

sections; which will produce a tendency towards the most economical utilization of the total resources available to science, both in brainpower and in money.

If "demand" may be seen as the "need" to sustain and advance the level of theoretical unity, and "supply" as the availability of techniques, deployed against this need, Polanyi's thought may be compressed within a model that on the surface resembles classical economics (see Figure 2.1).

Unlike the classical model, scientific opinion (as analogous to *price*) is never objectively dependent upon the ratio between "supply" and "demand." Rather, it is dependent upon what opinion leaders *perceive* that relation to be. *This is precisely the point at which Polanyi and the classical model diverge.* Polanyi insists that the quality of decisions made within the community of science, though uncoordinated by any formal authority, displays a deference to the opinions of eminent men — a condition that can only be explained by the classical model as an intrusion of "imperfect competition." These "chief Influentials," as Polanyi calls them, constantly monitor and redirect scientific interest so that the standards of professional performance in all branches of science are kept "approximately at an equal level."

By their advice they can either delay or accelerate the growth of a new line of research. They can provide special subsidies for new lines of research at any moment. By the award of prizes

Figure 2.1 How "Supply" (s) and "Demand" (d) Influence Scientific Opinion and the Acceptability Level of Scientific Theories (A)

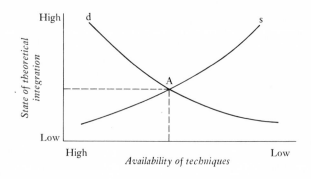

Figure 2.2

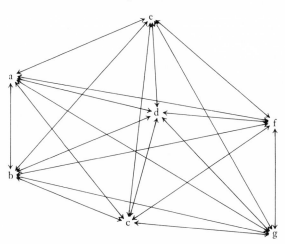

Each letter represents a decision-maker.
a ←——→ b refers to a *symmetric* relation in which a and b adjust decisions
to each other.

and of other distinctions, they can invest a promising pioneer
almost overnight with a position of authority and independence.
More slowly, but no less effectively, a new development can be
stimulated by the policy pursued by the Influentials in advising
on new appointments.[28]

For Polanyi, the decision-making structure that produces scientific opinion is composed of a network of mutual and "authoritative" adjustments in which some opinions are decidedly more
important than others. To diagram these relations we must distinguish between a system of response in which every decision-
maker adjusts directly to every other decision-maker (Smith's
position) and one in which opinion is coordinated by a combination of symmetric and asymmetric relations (Polanyi). Figure 2.2
represents the first, and Figure 2.3 the second.

In Figure 2.2 all decision-makers are potentially contributors to
collective opinion, and their ideas are mutually (symmetrically)
adjusted to each other. There are no hierarchical (asymmetric)

28 *Ibid.*, p. 54.

Figure 2.3

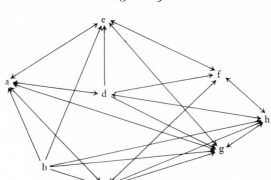

Each letter represents a decision-maker.
a ———→ b indicates that the direction of decision is from a single source (asymmetric).
a ←——→ b refers to symmetric relation where a and b adjust decisions to each other.

relations, no centrally regulated sources of decision. Each decision-maker is completely exposed and responsive to the opinion of every other decision-maker. The weight of *a*'s opinion is no greater than that of *g*, but when each opinion is adjusted to every other, a collective judgment or synthesis emerges. In Figure 2.3, however, there is a *combination* of symmetric and asymmetric relationships. The letters *b* and *d*, for example, symbolize decision-makers whose influence is more pervasive and asymmetric than that of *a*, *c*, *e*, *f*, *g*, or *h*. Of course *d*'s asymmetry is not perfect because of its adaptive response to *a* and *h*, but it is asymmetrical with the remaining decision-makers. In contrast, *b*'s asymmetry must be regarded as perfect, since it directs all the decision-makers within its range of contact.

Polanyi's concept of scientific opinion, therefore, emphasizes the interactive patterns of two distinctly different modes of response, although the asymmetric relationship is the more decisive and serves as a barometer of scientific opinion.

Polanyi's model of the organization of science, and those which in one way or another complement it,[29] are concerned with the

[29] See Harrison Brown's account of how the community of science reacts to theories that arise beyond the pale of professional scientific opinion.

"internal ecology of science." [30] Science is regarded as an autonomous community, alone competent to punish and reward claims to scientific originality and achievement. This model, as Polanyi suggests, is both "indicative" and "normative" — that is, both descriptive and prescriptive. It not only reports aspects of actual scientific behavior but urges that only through the autonomous self-coordination of science can high professional standards be maintained.

Polanyi's analysis lacks, however, an anticipation of how closely involved science may become with other institutions of society. Intimate relations could weaken the detachment and professionalism of scientific judgments with the result that paradigms of research might be influenced by the "ideological" purposes of organizations outside the scientific community. Although difficult to interpret, many of these conditions can be studied by exploring additional approaches to the organization of science that begin where Polanyi leaves off.

BIG SCIENCE AND THE LAWS OF
SOCIAL THERMODYNAMICS

One of the most arresting views of how the institutions of science respond to larger social and political purposes is furnished by Alvin Weinberg, Director of the Oak Ridge National Laboratory. Weinberg's perspective is embodied in his concept of "Thermodynamic Revolutions," [31] which assumes that the forces of change in the postindustrial world are those affecting levels of available energy and increasing semantic complexity.

Review of Immanuel Velikovsky's *Earth in Upheaval* in *Scientific American* 194, no. 3 (March 1956): 127–128. For a provocative insight into the activities of scientific research and the climate of opinion that surrounds accepted theories see Thomas S. Kuhn's analysis of "normal science," *The Structure of Scientific Revolutions* (Chicago: University of Chicago Press, 1962), especially p. 64. An interesting variation to Polanyi's position is found in D. J. de Solo Price, "The Science of Scientists," *Medical Opinion Review* 10 (1966): 88–97.

[30] The phrase "internal ecology of science" is used by Harvey Brooks in his explanation of Polanyi's concept of scientific organization; see *The Government of Science* (Cambridge, Mass.: The M.I.T. Press, 1968), p. 74.

[31] Alvin M. Weinberg, *Reflections on Big Science* (Cambridge, Mass.: The M.I.T. Press, 1967), p. 2.

The first represents an energy imbalance between the demands of society and the rate of energy accumulation. The solutions to problems found here deal largely with conversions from one system of physical energy to another, as sea water is converted into fresh water or atmospheric nitrogen into nitrate fertilizer.[32] The second force represents "an imbalance between the rate at which semantic stimuli — that is, information — are generated, and the rate at which the individual can respond to the stimuli." [33] More simply put, this means that as the sources of information increase in society, the individual has difficulty integrating the new information into his world and work.

Traditionally, energy levels were not related to the complexities of information,[34] but since Leo Szilard's brilliant essay in 1929 [35] — comparing information content and the decrease of entropy in a thermodynamic system — it has become increasingly fashionable to relate both energy and information to the laws of "classical" thermodynamics. Intrigued by this connection, Weinberg explicitly applies the first law of thermodynamics (which states that "energy can be neither created nor destroyed, only transformed from one form to another") [36] to his concept of energy levels, and the second law (which declares the entropy of the universe — that is, its state of disorder — to be always increasing) to his idea of semantic complexity.[37]

[32] *Ibid.*, p. 3.

[33] *Ibid.*, p. 4.

[34] For some interesting observations by political scientists concerning the relation of energy and information see: James G. Miller, "Toward a General Theory for the Behavioral Sciences" in Leonard D. White, ed., *The State of the Social Sciences* (Chicago: University of Chicago Press, 1956), p. 38; John T. Dorsey, Jr., "An Information-Energy Model" in Ferrel Heady and Sybil L. Stokes, eds., *Papers in Comparative Public Administration* (Ann Arbor, Mich.: Institute of Public Administration, 1962), p. 41; and Karl W. Deutsch, *Nationalism and Social Communication* (New York: Wiley, 1953), pp. 67–68.

[35] Leo Szilard, "Uber die Entropieverminderung in einem thermodynamischen System bei Eingriffen intelligenter Wesen," *Zeitschrift für Physik* 53 (1929): 840–856.

[36] Weinberg, *Reflections on Big Science*, p. 5.

[37] *Ibid.*

The conversion of energy requires knowledge of how science can be applied to social needs. But semantic complexity is basic to how all scientific knowledge is certified, preserved, and disseminated. Unlike *energy imbalance*, semantic complexity cannot be solved by creating technological processes that convert one form of energy to another. The semantic problem is much more delicate, since it involves "the individual's capacity to understand and the proliferation of his semantic environment." [38] When compared to the notion of energy levels, "the imbalance between the proliferating semantic environment and the individual's semantic mechanism is less clear, partly because the technology of information is younger, and partly because the problem of the proliferating semantic environment is more complex." [39]

Despite these difficulties, Weinberg applies the idea of semantic complexity to the development of specialized fields of scientific inquiry. The world of science, he argues, has become incomprehensible in its larger contours because the fragmentation of research has confined each scientist to a narrow field.[40] As this specialization continues, fields of interest become narrower and the number of people who can integrate related specialities declines. The immediate danger is loss of professional efficiency, but the long-term damage is that science must further remove itself from the world by advancing to higher levels of abstraction. As Weinberg explains,

> Growth and fragmentation impair the efficiency of science by forcing science to become a team activity, because a single knowledgeable mind is in many ways a more efficient instrument than is a collection of minds that possess an equal total sum of relevant knowledge. . . . As science fragments, it seeks to reintegrate itself by moving to a higher level of abstraction. Quantum mechanics implies the details of the Balmer series in hydrogen; topology now unifies certain aspects of nonlinear differential equations; the Watson-Crick model unifies many parts of biology. But the unification is at a higher level of abstraction. Knowing the relativistic Dirac equation is not the same as sens-

[38] *Ibid.*, p. 25.
[39] *Ibid.*, p. 26.
[40] *Ibid.*, p. 42.

ing and feeling the Balmer lines showing darkly in the sun's spectrum.[41]

Progressive abstraction becomes the only way in which science can reintegrate itself to cope with increasing specialization. Matters once grasped immediately, almost existentially, must now be grasped *in principle*.[42] But knowing in principle is not the same as knowing from experience,[43] for as "one moves to a higher level of abstraction, one omits something, either because applying a complete theory to a detailed situation would go beyond our mathematics (we cannot deduce the energy levels of U^{iv} from quantum theory) or because our original theory omits something initially (we have many models of the nucleus, but each model is inadequate in some respect)." [44]

The price of increasing abstraction is paid by an increase in specialized terminology and abstruse conceptualization, which are not a part of routine scientific experience.[45] The immediate effect is that fewer and fewer scientists are capable of understanding theoretical problems outside their own areas of research. "Thus in a practical sense, mathematics, at the same time it is becoming conceptually more unified, is fragmenting at this higher level of abstraction simply because those whose fields are receiving the benefits of the unification are incapable of communicating with their unifiers." [46] Weinberg is just as insistent that every other field of scientific work is undergoing similar strains.

The unification of scientific knowledge at high levels of abstraction creates conditions that stress the "changeability of scientific fashions." [47] Fragmentation of traditional scientific knowledge follows the curve of active research interest from discipline to discipline. Sometimes a field is abandoned because all its important problems appear to be solved — as in classical thermodynamics

[41] *Ibid.*, pp. 43–44.

[42] *Ibid.*, p. 44.

[43] See Michael Oakeshott's distinction between theoretical and technical knowledge in *Rationalism in Politics*.

[44] Weinberg, *Reflections on Big Science*, pp. 44–45.

[45] *Ibid.*, p. 45.

[46] *Ibid.*

[47] *Ibid.*

or Newtonian mechanics — or because it becomes virtually impossible to make further progress — as happened in super-conductivity prior to the discovery of the isotope effect.[48] Perhaps even more to the point, fields no longer actively pursued in one discipline become matters of intense interest in others, creating additional problems for the continuity of scientific knowledge. Weinberg speaks to this state of affairs with force and candor:

> Very typically [he urges] a field that was once fashionable eventually ceases to command the interest of the scientists in that field. . . . Nuclear chemistry is a good example of this trend: it began as nuclear physics, was taken over by chemists, and now, insofar as nuclear properties of radionuclides are important for technology, parts of nuclear chemistry are being taken over by engineers. This tendency for fashions in science to come and go greatly complicates the teaching of science. For, as science proliferates, the discrepancy tends to widen between the older, consolidated body of scientific knowledge and the parts of science that excite the active researcher.[49]

The impact of specialization upon the unity of science forces Weinberg to recognize a problem basic to politics — the use of remote but "authoritative" symbols in maintaining order. In fact, his account of the growing distance between abstractions of science and physical reality parallels John Schaar's description of man's evolving political estate.

> At the dawn of civilization, men lived closer to the deepest realities of communal life than we ever can. Knowledge which they grasped immediately, almost physically, we grasp only by the hardest work and thought; and, even then, our grasp sometimes seems weak and our vision narrow, when set alongside theirs. . . . The men of the first cities each day could see the high wall which separated their city from the chaos of nature outside it. They knew their city and its defining wall were works of art, not products of nature, tiny islands of order surrounded by nature's vast wildness. Being so close to experience they could report their knowledge in the vivid concrete language of experi-

48 *Ibid.*, p. 46.
49 *Ibid.*

ence, as poets still do, rather than in the drier, more remote language of the detached and observing intellect. . . .[50]

Fragmentation and abstraction in science are apparently inevitable. But the tensions produced in reconciling the achievements of scientific innovation (which are related to fragmentation and abstraction) and the general tradition of scientific knowledge create demands for the social reorganization of science. Weinberg's greatest achievements are his suggestions for reorganizing the scientific community (to avert the disaster of information overload) and his sensitivity to the prospects of scientific choice that engage the institutions of larger society.

Although not entirely original,[51] Weinberg's proposals are directed toward synthesizing information within the scientific community and creating liaison channels between science and the larger society. It is no longer possible, Weinberg thinks, for science to pretend that it can coordinate itself through a system of spontaneous adjustment. The complexities of specialized research have closed off equal access to information — both practical and theoretical — that is assumed as the starting point by the self-coordination model. The solution for science must be found in some hierarchical order, but one with great flexibility and limited interference from the top. The upper strata of science, Weinberg feels, should be occupied by men who are distinguished neither by institutional power nor personal rhetoric, but by their ability to synthesize work in several related specialties.

Structurally, the organization of science should be composed of three levels.[52] The first level would consist of bench scientists who are highly skilled in the conduct of their research but whose range of "outside" contact is small. The achievements of this group would be monitored — for content and application — by a second group that Weinberg refers to as "group leaders or

[50] John Schaar, *Escape from Authority* (New York: Basic Books, 1961), p. 291.

[51] The plan was suggested by Eugene P. Wigner in an article entitled "The Limits of Science," *Proceedings of the American Philosophical Society* 94 (1950): 422–427.

[52] Weinberg, *Reflections on Big Science*, p. 47.

Figure 2.4 WEINBERG'S CONCEPT OF "HIGHER-ORDER SURVEILLANCE" WITHIN |THE| SCIENTIFIC COMMUNITY[a]

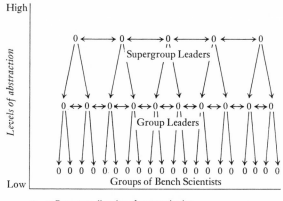

← → Represents direction of communication

↓ Represents direction of surveillance

[a] The diagram is based upon an interpretation of Weinberg's description.

bosses." The group leaders would be in constant communication with one another and could "maintain contact between different groups of bench scientists." The third level would find "super-group leaders" watching the group bosses and integrating an even greater span of scientific research. As Weinberg characterizes it:

> This proposed hierarchical structure for science corresponds to a separation into different levels of abstraction which is reminiscent of Alfred Korzybski's "Structural Differential." The traditional working scientists are at the bottom rung — each one knows almost everything about almost nothing; as one progresses to the top of the ladder, the subject matter becomes more abstract until one finally reaches the philosopher at the top who knows almost nothing about almost everything.[53]

Weinberg insists that while the formal relations of the model (see Figure 2.4) are largely normative, there are indications that "higher order surveillance" is partially descriptive of recent de-

53 *Ibid.*

velopments within the scientific community itself. There are
some quantum chemists, for example, who maintain contact with
panels of quantum organic chemists and biochemists, and who
can interpret and correlate the theoretical work being done in
all three disciplines. Likewise, theoretical physicists and theoretical chemists perform an integrative function for wide areas in
physics and chemistry. To a much smaller extent the theoretical
biologist plays an integrative role for the growing biological
specialties.[54]

Each level of surveillance or integration, Weinberg argues, is
indicative of a process of *systematized induction*, where "the cor-
relation of many seemingly disparate facts and the identification
of regularity in a sea of diversity" fall to group leaders and super-
group leaders.[55] In this way

> science has . . . begun to invent new institutions that corre-
> spond to this social layering of scientists into sifters and inter-
> preters on the one hand and collectors and inventors on the
> other. The scientists who collect and sift the facts would in our
> modern terminology make up a "specialized information center,"
> that is, a group of scientists who, in a narrow, well-defined field
> of science, collect, sift, and interpret information for other work-
> ers in the field.[56]

This integrative function provides coherence to scientific knowledge and helps restrain tendencies to disorder.

The trend toward complexity and the demands of society for
new forms of energy have divided scientific effort into activities
of scale.[57] Self-sustaining research that conforms to the internal
values of the scientific community is known as Little Science,
whereas work that requires elaborate equipment and large staffs
and depends upon outside sources of support is called Big Science.[58] Both scales of inquiry, however, have grown explosively
in recent years. It is therefore quite realistic to speak of Little

54 *Ibid.*, p. 48.
55 *Ibid.*, p. 51.
56 *Ibid.*, pp. 51–52.
57 *Ibid.*, p. 39.
58 *Ibid.*

Science as having imposing structural dimensions. The essential difference between Big and Little Science is not that they cover different areas of inquiry, but that one demands a greater commitment of resources from society and is more responsive to social needs.

Under present conditions there is a tendency to regard Big Science as the norm of scientific research. Enormous prestige is associated with the administration of large funds and great numbers of people — to say nothing of the experiments and technologies made possible by such an investment. Moreover, it is difficult for Little Science to resist the habits of Big Science because Little Scientists talk to Big Scientists and are enchanted by the possibilities of large-scale projects and sustained public support.[59] These contacts and the demands of public opinion for "socially relevant" research affect the validity of science by introducing additional criteria for decision-making. The internal (or professional) criteria for choice — amounting to judgments within scientific fields on what areas to expand and on which scientists are competent to develop them — must adapt to powerful external

[59] Weinberg dramatizes this condition by commenting upon certain aspects of the new style of biological research. He observes:

> In earlier times, when biology was par excellence Little Science, biologists were content to look only at those problems that could be handled in the manner of Little Science. Genetics was done with fruit flies, with their large chromosomes, because fruit flies are inexpensive, not because fruit flies are as much like man as are mammals. Those questions that required large protocols of expensive animals were answered poorly or not at all, not because the questions were unimportant, but because to answer them was expensive and required the style of Big Science, which was so foreign to the biologists' tradition. *But this is changing, in part at least, because the Big Scientists from neighboring fields have taught the habit of Big Science to the biologists.* Perhaps the best-known example of the drastically changed style of some biological research is the large-scale mouse genetics experiment of W. L. Russell at Oak Ridge. For the past sixteen years Russell has been studying the genetic effects of ionizing radiation in a mammal, the mouse. Since mutations even at high dose rates are so rare, Russell uses colonies containing 100,000 mice. To perform such experiments takes money and many people, and yet it seems impossible to visualize any other way of obtaining the data. [emphasis mine]

Ibid., p. 107.

criteria that come from neighboring scientific disciplines and the public at large.

Weinberg recognizes three external criteria that influence the direction and validity of scientific inquiry. These are *technological merit*, *scientific merit*, and *social merit*. Technological merit amounts to deciding what technological possibilities are worthwhile — either for making a piece of basic research relevant or for fulfilling certain social aims — and supporting the research necessary to achieve those ends.[60] Scientific merit is concerned with comprehensive judgments about the potential value of a field of scientific research. Weinberg insists on these assessments being weighted in favor of those fields that "contribute . . . most heavily and illuminate . . . most brightly" the activities in neighboring disciplines.[61] In practice, this principle is analogous to the one used by a project director who has the responsibility for completing a nuclear reactor on schedule. His decisions must balance the relative advantages of component development and fundamental research so that both contribute to the project's goals.[62] Finally, social merit introduces into scientific activity questions about human welfare and the values of man.[63] As a performance standard, or as a guide to prospective areas of research, social merit is the most difficult criterion of all to implement. As Weinberg asks, "Who is to define the values of man, or even the values of our society?"[64] Yet, assuming for a moment that these matters can be successfully overcome, an additional problem remains: What scientific or technological effort may be regarded as a commitment to further the general values of society?

The ultimate content of these criteria is likely never to be explicit. In fact, all Weinberg has done is focus upon the types of social influence that science may face as it increases its scope and appeals to society for continued support. The extent to

[60] *Ibid.*, pp. 72–73.
[61] *Ibid.*, p. 75.
[62] *Ibid.*
[63] *Ibid.*, pp. 75–76.
[64] *Ibid.*, p. 76.

which these forces condition the substance of scientific inquiry is uncertain, but at the very least, Weinberg has suggested a pattern of development with important social implications for scientific inquiry (see Figure 2.5).

SCIENCE AS AN ESTATE OF THE REALM

The assumption made thus far is that the organizational structure of scientific inquiry has a conditioning effect upon the certification of scientific knowledge. For this reason it matters who is accredited to participate in scientific work and where their loyalties may ultimately lie. Professionalized science has traditionally anticipated very modest interference from the outside, relying almost exclusively upon the internal dynamics of specialized communication to register acceptable research paradigms, fields of scientific investment, and admissible hypotheses. But if Weinberg's analysis is correct — if continued large-scale support of science must meet external criteria for choice — scientific inquiry may be entering a *paraprofessional* phase that could have serious repercussions for the development of scientific knowledge. The integration of scientific research into the activities and purposes of larger society means that pro-

Figure 2.5 AN INTERPRETATION OF WEINBERG'S CONCEPTION OF THE RELATIONSHIP BETWEEN THE SCALE OF SCIENTIFIC AND SOCIAL PURPOSE

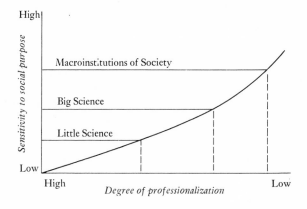

fessionalized science must directly respond to competitive systems of perception (such as religion or political ideology) which may question or even distort its contents.

It is precisely this prospect that worries Michael Polanyi and makes him sensitive to the invasion of autonomous science by either the representatives of economic and technological viewpoints or by the state. His vision of a *paraprofessional* science begins and ends in distrust and apprehension. He consistently argues that the viability of scientific knowledge depends upon an internal (professionalized) system of mutual adjustment and control, immune to concerns about the benefits of research to mankind. Polanyi's anxiety is only intensified by the paraprofessional inferences that can be drawn from Weinberg's Theory of Thermodynamic Revolutions. For at the center of this concept is the premise that science must respond to social needs and accept external criteria for many of its decisions.

The third argument about the place of professionalized science in modern society is suggested by *constitutional relativism.* Perhaps the most polished and prudent representative of this idea is Don K. Price, whose active participation in the creation of the Atomic Energy Commission and the National Science Foundation gives him firsthand knowledge of the actual conditions under which government and science interact. Price's position is complex, since he is aware, first of all, of the multiple and unrelated levels of scientific activity, and second, of a governmental structure which is pluralistic and responsive to a variety of different constituencies. His central concern, however, is with the external relations of science. These, he feels, while representing the intellectual products of specialized and highly diverse inquiries, increasingly resemble a "loosely defined estate with a special function in our constitutional system." [65]

In its contact with larger society the scientific estate is distinguished neither by formal political office nor by economic or class interests. Rather it is a community of training and skill,[66]

[65] Don Price, *The Scientific Estate* (Cambridge, Mass.: The Belknap Press of Harvard University, 1965), p. 20.
[66] *Ibid.,* p. 135.

whose service, Price believes, is absolutely essential for resolving the major problems that confront society today. The representatives of this community, however, have access to cognitive resources denied to others, and as they begin to emerge as full-fledged participants in society, they create anxieties about the responsibility of their actions and the scope of their influence. On matters of public support for science or in defining common social problems, what members of the scientific estate do or say has important implications for the balances of power which characterize the social system. Price feels that these relations constitute the "politics of science" and lead scientists into arenas of national policy making.

In an attempt to clarify these matters, Price argues that in its purest form science is occupied exclusively with the pursuit of knowledge and truth, and politics with the problems of power and action. Thus, the closer the scientific estate lies "to the end of the spectrum that is concerned solely with truth, the more it is entitled to freedom and self-government; and . . . the closer it gets to the exercise of power, the less it is permitted to organize itself as a corporate entity, and the more it is required to submit to the test of political responsibility, in the sense of submitting to the ultimate decision of the electorate." [67]

This simple division of labor and intent is the key to Price's whole outlook toward the "politics of science," for along the "spectrum from truth to power" he discovers countervailing estates that keep the activities of science from moving beyond their proper sphere of influence. In addition to the scientists themselves, whose central purpose is the discovery and dissemination of truth, there are other estates composed of professionals, administrators, and politicians.[68] The professionals try to apply the truth of science to narrow-gauge social purposes such as the construction of highways or providing medical attention. Administrators control the vast nonelective bureaucracies of government and business and, in varying degrees, are responsible for carrying out both small- and large-scale social goals. They do not, how-

[67] *Ibid.*, p. 137.
[68] *Ibid.*, pp. 132–136.

ever, rely upon any specialized body of knowledge or restricted fields of research to accomplish their tasks. "On the contrary," Price argues, "[they] must be prepared to understand and use a wide variety of professional expertise and scholarly disciplines, as [they] help [their] political superiors (or the directors of a business corporation) attain their general purposes." [69] Politicians are the farthest removed from the "inhuman abstractions" of science and the pursuit of demonstrable truth. Although they employ "the skills of administrators and engineers and scientists . . . in the end they make their most important decisions on the basis of value judgements or hunch or compromise or power interests." [70]

From these descriptions it is not surprising that Price wishes the four estates to be taken as "arbitrary groupings along a rather muddled spectrum." [71] But it is disappointing that he confines the "politics of science" to those relations involving scientists in recognized forums of policy making, particularly since he is clearly aware that prevailing systems of thought within the scientific community are dependent upon acknowledged groups of oligarchs. He explicitly argues, for example, that

> most scientists are prepared to work most of the time within the framework of ideas developed by their acknowledged leaders. In that sense, within any discipline, science is ruled by oligarchs who hold influence as long as their concepts and systems are accepted as the most successful strategy. . . . Once in a great while, a rival system is proposed; then there can usually be no compromise between the two ways of viewing reality, and no settlement of the issue by majority opinion. The metaphor of "scientific revolution" suggests the way in which the losing party is displaced from authority, discredited, and its doctrines eliminated from textbooks.[72]

Yet he is unwilling to draw from these observations the inference that the oligarchs of science are actually committed to something

[69] *Ibid.*, pp. 133–134.
[70] *Ibid.*, p. 134.
[71] *Ibid.*, p. 192.
[72] *Ibid.*, p. 172.

called the politics of knowledge – the removal of epistemic uncertainty through argument, recommendation, partisan discussion,
authoritative prescription, and other techniques of influence and
persuasion. Rather, Price takes an institutional view of politics,
in which "estates of the realm" replace individual actors as right-
ful participants in "public" controversy. The political aspects of
science are therefore confined to relations with other large estates
that engage in a depersonalized struggle for power and are held
in check by external mechanisms of control.

This is, of course, the fundamental perspective from which
such constitutional theorists as Harrington, Locke, Hume,
Montesquieu, and Madison have taken their bearings. Price really
offers nothing new. His main thought is still institutional balance,
protected by an ideological commitment to equilibrium and a
political constitution of divided responsibilities and dispersed
powers. The prevailing balances under these conditions (Price's
"constitutional relativity") depend, first of all, upon the operational (but unwritten) rules that describe the kind of equilibrium
to be achieved, and second, upon the levels of access to different
centers of governmental power.

Given this point of view, Price quite easily maintains that the
four estates are held to their power spheres by informal rules or
"mutual defenses" which govern their relations. In his judgment
these "defenses" amount to an endorsement of the following
imperatives:

1. A respect for the self-government of university departments
that are devoted to scientific inquiry.

2. An acknowledgment that the professions are dependent
upon the objectivity and reliability of scientific data.

3. An awareness by politicians and administrators that they
must rely upon scientists and professionals for objective knowledge.

4. A recognition that the procedural restrictions to scientific
and professional accreditation must not be interfered with by
the politicians.[73]

---

[73] *Ibid.*, pp. 195–196.

These norms, moreover, are structurally reinforced by a constitutional system characterized by a "general division of power between a legislature and an executive, each holding tenure independently of the other." [74] Whether in the committees of Congress, in the White House Office, or in an administrative bureau, countervailing support can usually be secured against the possibility of any estate's becoming predominant. The great virtue of our *political* system, as Price describes it, is that it takes advantage of pluralist tendencies by impersonally bending the disparate motives of each estate into a grand consensus. Although impossible to state explicitly, the content of this consensus becomes visible against a background of constitutional relativity. Hence:

> The balance within the constitutional system between the estates that draw their power from scientific knowledge and those that depend on legal authority is necessarily a relative one. No fixed and mechanical system could survive in an era in which science forces such rapid changes in the structure of the economy. But within a tradition that protects the mutual independence of the legislature and the executive, the new strength of the scientific and professional estates can serve to safeguard the pluralism and freedom of the constitutional system. . . . We are protected by our consensus that science and politics in a free system, while freely interacting through the professions and administration, have to be maintained as mutually independent estates, each able to check and criticize the other.[75]

SCIENCE AS A TERTIARY INDUSTRY

The boldest attack against the exclusiveness of scientific inquiry, and one in favor of expanding its paraprofessional dimensions, is provided by Stephen Toulmin.[76] Toulmin urges that the role of contemporary science cannot be adequately anticipated by relying upon either the autonomy argument (Polanyi), including its permutation by Price, or Weinberg's

---

[74] *Ibid.*, p. 197.

[75] *Ibid.*, pp. 204–205.

[76] Stephen Toulmin, "The Complexity of Scientific Choice II: Culture, Overheads, or Tertiary Industry?" *Minerva* 4, no. 2 (Winter 1966): 155–169.

Theory of Thermodynamic Revolutions. Rather, science must be seen as a *tertiary industry*, whose "productive output," in conventional language, is nonexistent,[77] but whose operations are directed toward fulfilling a variety of social needs.

This is an unusual perspective, and one largely dependent upon a "post affluent" assessment of productivity and public investment. Less developed systems of economic activity are persistently confronted with problems of scarcity. This is true both of economies dominated by *primary industries* — industries producing new materials directly, such as agriculture and mining — and of those typified by *secondary industries*, where basic materials are processed into salable commodities. *Tertiary industries*, however, are by-products of material abundance; they do not produce commodities at all, but exist for the employment of institutional resources. As Toulmin says,

> A century and a half ago, the vast mass of the work-force in all countries was employed in agriculture, forestry, mining and fishing — *primary* industries. Only during the last 50 years has the proportion of the work-force so engaged in the major industrialized countries dropped sharply, from well over 1:2 to something less than 1:10. To begin with, though with periodic lapses, the labourers who were not needed for *primary* production found occupation in manufacturing industry and in the associated clerical and service trades. They did not themselves produce new materials directly, but they did process them into salable objects — or else they engaged in other activities (e.g., bookkeeping, stock-taking, trucking, cleaning, maintenance) ancillary to such processing. So there came about the age of the *secondary industries*. But, in time, this age too will prove to have been only one phase in economic history. . . . If this thumbnail picture of recent economic history has any justice in it, then the central economic problem of the coming age will not be one of *output*, but one of *employment*.[78]

In the coming economic age, thrift and hard work, the traditional virtues of an economy of scarcity, will be replaced by values emphasizing the importance of institutional needs — that is,

[77] *Ibid.*, p. 167.
[78] *Ibid.*, pp. 163–164.

organizational growth and protection rather than any measurable standard of production. Science as a tertiary industry points to this possibility, although its immediate goal is simply the mobilization of employment opportunities. Toulmin can thus forcefully assert:

> Pure scientific research is, and can deliberately be chosen to be, one of those new, *tertiary* activities by which employment and prosperity can be maintained in an industrialized society, even after both primary and secondary industries have become too *efficient* to occupy the available labour-force. A scientific research laboratory can serve, just as well as a manufacturing enterprise, as the focus around which the life and prosperity of a community can be organized. To hazard a social prophecy, one can well imagine the "laboratory town" becoming as characteristic a feature of late twentieth-century social life as the "mill town" was in the mid-nineteenth century.[79]

The importance of Toulmin's argument is its focus upon the activities of science in a much wider setting than previous examples. In his view, professionalized science will become increasingly integrated into the purposive institutions of society and will respond to a greater variety of political pressures. Although intriguing, this prospect carries both promise and danger: the promise of a unique commitment by science to areas of research that may make life more comfortable, stimulating, and secure; the danger that science may become just another social instrument with no higher purpose than aggregating resources for the dominant institutions of society.

THE RELATIVE SCOPE OF SCIENCE

The emphasis that Toulmin places upon the "socialization" of science anticipates an open play of political forces upon the direction of scientific inquiry. If that proves accurate, professionalized science must struggle against outside influences which may redeploy the main lines of scientific interest. One could argue, of course, that the professionalized aspects of science are in a developmental stage that will ultimately point to some form of structural union with other elements in

[79] *Ibid.*, p. 164.

society. After all, as Figure 2.6 reveals, each approach presented thus far has some areas of structural overlap. But do these similarities represent a rudimentary pattern of organizational development? Do they suggest that professionalized science is just a phase in the structural maturation of society? Certainly it is too early to give a positive endorsement of that view, but if a developmental explanation is impossible, it must be made clear that each of these "models" sustains a different pattern of "politics." The "politics of science" within Polanyi's autonomy model differ structurally from the political dynamics that Toulmin's model anticipates, for Polanyi views the organization of science as essentially small,

Figure 2.6 SPATIAL DIMENSIONS OF SCIENCE

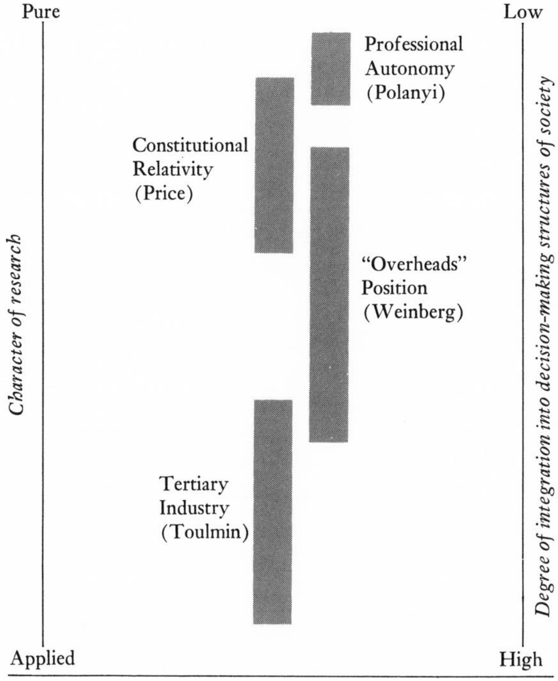

Bars represent the relative positions of the four spatial models of science by the character of their research and the degree of integration into the decision-making structures of society.

encompassing few interests, and committed to a narrow range of achievement, while Toulmin sees the interests of science as closely associated with the purposes of society, responsive to a variety of interests, and devoted ultimately to enlarging the opportunities of man. From this perspective, the organizational features of science determine the social dimensions of inquiry — and hence the number and kind of competing pressures that are a part of scientific research.

Perhaps much of the confusion presently surrounding the relationship of science to politics can be eliminated if the organizational *scope* of scientific activity can be kept relatively distinct. While theoretically essential, this is difficult to accomplish, for there are multiple levels of scientific focus and involvement, some of which are closely related to the macroinstitutions of government and industry. There are doubtless many ways of conceptualizing these relations, but the four simple models of scope presented here do illustrate the proposition that science may occupy different spatial dimensions and that, with increasing "size," the character of its politics must change.

This argument should occasion no surprise. The idea of *scope* is familiar to political scientists, although its implications for scientific inquiry have not been systematically explored. Madison, for example, in *Federalist X* convincingly argues that organizational scope is vital to an understanding of politics within a pluralistic society.

> The smaller the society, the fewer probably will be the distinct parties and interests composing it, the more frequently will a majority be found of the same party; and the smaller number of individuals composing a majority, the smaller the compass within which they are placed, the more easily they will concert and execute their plans of oppression. Extend the sphere and you take in a greater variety of parties and interests; you make it less probable that a majority of the whole will have a common motive to invade the rights of other citizens.[80]

More recently E. E. Schattschneider has given detailed attention to the politics of scope. He ingeniously suggests that the result of

[80] *The Federalist*, Max Beloff, ed. (New York: Macmillan, 1948), pp. 46–47.

all political conflict is determined by the spatial dimensions relevant to it.

> The first proposition is that the outcome of every conflict is determined by the *extent* to which the audience becomes involved in it. That is, the outcome of all conflict is determined by the *scope* of its contagion. The number of people involved in any conflict determines what happens; every change in the number of participants, every increase or reduction in the number of participants affects the result.[81]

Schattschneider does insist, however, that "there is nothing intrinsically good or bad about any given scope of conflict"; one must only be aware that with each new extension there is "a new pattern of competition, a new balance of forces and a new result." [82]

These remarks are given additional force by Sheldon Wolin's brilliant treatment of the emergence of political space as a theoretical concept in political philosophy. His comments help define not only the importance of space for political inquiry, but also the means by which a society tries to structure its space to avoid conflict.

> The metaphysical categories resident in political theory can be illustrated by the notion of political space. One might begin by pointing out how this had its origin in the ancient world in the evolution of national consciousness. The Hebraic idea of a separate people, the Greek distinction between Hellene and barbarian, the Roman pride in *Romanitas*, the mediaeval notion of Christendom, all contributed to sharpen the sense of distinctive identity which then became associated with a determinate geographic area and a particular culture.
>
> But the concept of political space turned on more than a distinction between the "inside" of a specific and differentiated context of actions and events and an "outside" that was largely unknown and undifferentiated. It involved also the crucial question of the arrangements for settling the problems arising out of the fact that a large number of human beings, possessing a com-

---

[81] E. E. Schattschneider, *The Semi-Sovereign People* (New York: Holt, Rinehart & Winston, 1960), p. 2.

[82] *Ibid.*, pp. 17–18.

mon cultural identity, occupied the same determinate area. [Moreover, if we could see political space as an arena where] the plans, ambitions, and actions of individuals and groups incessantly jar against each other — colliding, blocking, coalescing, separating — we could better appreciate the ingenious role of these arrangements in reducing frictions. By a variety of means, a society seeks to structure its space: by systems of rights and duties, class and social distinctions, legal and extralegal restraints and inhibitions, favors and punishments, permissions and tabus. These arrangements serve to mark out paths along which human motions can proceed harmlessly or beneficially.[83]

According to Wolin two imperatives must be fulfilled if political space is to exist. First, there must be an awareness that what is circumscribed possesses a "distinctive identity" — that is, a structural differentiation that persists through time. Second, there must be "internal" arrangements for settling problems that grow out of a sense of common preoccupation and direction. Since either of these requirements may eventually fail, political space is potentially volatile. As Wolin points out, "political space becomes a problem when human energies cannot be controlled by existing arrangements." [84] This might be the result of difficulties surrounding the internal machinery for problem-solving, or it might be a matter of external pressure too great to withstand or forestall. In any event, political space must be understood as an artificial creation, maintained in the face of both internal and external tendencies to disorder or rearrangement.

Yet the idea of political space is not intrinsically revolutionary. It is part of the traditional luggage of political theory, although its dimensions are usually described by synonyms. For example, instead of indicating the "size" of political space, such terms as "city," "state," "nation," "pressure group," or perhaps even "corporation" are used. Unfortunately, since science is not structurally differentiated by a long social tradition, its spatial dimensions are somewhat unsettled. The four models of science

[83] Sheldon S. Wolin, *Politics and Vision* (Boston: Little, Brown, 1960), p. 16.
[84] *Ibid.*, p. 17.

presented reflect this sense of inconstancy, for they represent different ways of perceiving scientific activity. Within each model there are not only differences in patterns of politics, but also consequential differences in the way the goals of science are perceived. Toulmin's idea of science as a "tertiary industry" differs starkly from Polanyi's insistence that it is an autonomous profession, yet both views have received enthusiastic support and both point to developments that can claim to be real.

As information increases about scientific activity, its spatial dimensions may assume more determinate relations. Perhaps a single structural framework or template can be developed for science that will cast its different levels of instrumental perception and social action into some recognizable pattern. But this possibility seems remote. The immediate problems of understanding science involve how each model of science perceives the external world and what it does with the information received. Each view of scientific "reality" will vary as the "political space" of science expands or contracts, for each alteration in scope is accompanied by either an addition or diminution in demands and interests that condition scientific perception.[85]

---

[85] The most convincing account known to me of science as a system of perception is found in David Bohm's *The Special Theory of Relativity*, pp. 185-230. Although he does not comment upon the political factors that might influence perception, his observations are quite relevant. He argues, for example:

> The interesting point that has emerged from a simultaneous consideration of what has developed in modern science and of what has been disclosed in modern studies of the process of perception is that the new ideas required to understand the both of them are rather similar. . . . this similarity is not accidental but rather has a deep reason behind it. The reason . . . is that scientific investigation is basically a mode of extending our *perception* of the world, and not mainly a mode of obtaining *knowledge* about it. That is to say, while science does involve a search for knowledge, the essential role of this knowledge is that it is an adjunct to an extended perceptual process. And if science is basically such a mode of perception, then, as we shall try to show, it is quite reasonable that certain essential features of scientific research shall be rather similar to corresponding features of immediate perception. (pp. 218-219)

In support of his position Bohm suggests that the similarity between scientific research and individual perception has been anticipated by at least two

Since many different social influences contribute to the models of nature that scientists create, the autonomous profession has been selected as the spatial dimension within which they can be more fully explored. Social and political factors do account for an important part of scientific perception and thus help build up our impressions of external reality. Of course, they are not the only influences — even at this level of "space." Various kinds of artificial instrumentation (the microscope, the telescope, the cyclotron, the bubble chamber, to use obvious examples) also aid in creating models of nature, and they too must be seen as manipulative tools of scientific inquiry. Although this study does not analyze the interaction between the physical world and all techniques for extending scientific perception, Marshall Walker has brilliantly demonstrated how both the instrumentation of science and social "devices" are combined in the "research cycle." By diagramming their relations, he further clarifies social and political influences upon professionalized science (Figure 2.7). His analysis begins with classic parsimony:

> Let us consider a particular instance of an astronomer studying a star. A star P emits a light wave PC_1 which travels through space and is incident on a spectrograph PA_1, which analyzes the light into a spectrum and records on a photographic plate. This plate is examined by an experimenter using a light wave PC_2 which is incident on the retina R of the observer and gives rise to a pattern of nerve impulses N which reach the brain B and are filed.
>
> Previously other individuals S have written books SA_1 which are read and give rise to signal patterns SC_2 which affect the retina R and, through the nerves N, reach the brain B and are filed.
>
> The arrival of a problem signal from either P or S activates the brain to a scanning search of its files, which continues until the problem is solved or later signals relax the search. This search process turns up idealized parts of the original data (abstractions), and some of these abstractions are used as basic categories to construct a model M.

---

distinguished scholars: N. H. Hanson, *Patterns of Discovery* (New York: Cambridge University Press, 1958), and Thomas Kuhn, *The Structure of Scientific Revolutions*.

Figure 2.7 THE RESEARCH CYCLE

Diagram showing how feedback from the physical and social world provides a self-correcting system for the production of models that have correspondences to the external world.

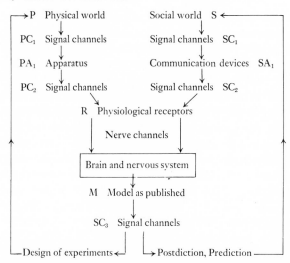

Source: Marshall Walker, *The Nature of Scientific Thought*, © 1963, p. 78. Reprinted by permission of Prentice-Hall, Inc., Englewood Cliffs, N.J.

Model M is described in a scientific journal SC_3 and predictions are made. These predictions . . . refer back to the social world S of other individuals, who compare them to their stored records of physical data and emit signals SC_1 of praise or blame. By either route there is a feedback of influence which reshapes the model M and the cycle repeats.[86]

Walker's comments on social influences as part of scientific perception are necessarily schematic and theoretical. Now the social parameters of science must be explored from a more empirical perspective — the task of the following chapter.

[86] Marshall Walker, *The Nature of Scientific Thought* (Englewood Cliffs, N.J.: Prentice-Hall, 1963), pp. 77–79.

3

The social parameters
of the autonomous system

Francis Bacon once complained that "never any knowledge was delivered in the same order it was invented." He might well have been speaking of contemporary science which purposefully seems to ignore the social milieu in which the work was done. Reading scientific treatises is like moving through the observations of disembodied intellects — no passion or struggle is visible on the surface. In fact, most accounts of scientific research indicate little awareness that human competition for place or reward or recognition by one's peers constitutes a meaningful part of scientific behavior.[1]

Beneath this placid exterior, however, is a subterranean scientific world of conflict and movement, a world characterized not by abstract and dispassionate discussion, but by activities which

---

[1] Although not characteristic of the entire sample, an inorganic chemist responded to the survey questionnaire by saying: "In many cases the motives of scientists are human ones — and thus out of place."

are both selfish and aggressive – a world victimized by the *idols* of thought Bacon hoped he could erase.[2]

In the previous chapter, it was suggested that the institutional processes inherent in scientific inquiry change as alterations in "social space" become apparent. If professionalized science is examined from the "spatial dimension" of a "closed" and autonomous system, its social parameters begin to emerge when an answer is given to the following question: what institutions provide science with means for subsistence and reproduction? Although diverse possibilities exist (for example, foundations, industries, governments, universities), the essential conditions of autonomy are provided by the universities. This means that both financial security and recruitment opportunities are given to scientists who operate within these confines. But that is not all. Certain patterns of social behavior and awareness are much more frequently found in university-based science than in scientific activity that takes place elsewhere. In this chapter a "contour map" of the autonomous system is created by exploring two areas in which its social activities are both visible and compelling. These deal with (1) the structural characteristics of scientific research; and (2) the social norms of scientific inquiry.

THE STRUCTURAL CHARACTERISTICS
OF SCIENTIFIC RESEARCH

In the United States the basic organizational unit of scientific inquiry is the university department. As Warren Hagstrom has pointed out, "a well-established scientific discipline requires university departments consigned to it." [3] True, scientific

---

[2] Bacon's use of the word *idol* refers to conceptual "prejudices" that are characteristic of the human condition. They enchant thought with *images* of the world and prevent a true understanding of reality. Today we would probably use the word *reification* in place of *idol*, but the essential point remains: thought processes are highly influenced by habits of perceptual inference that are derived from man's social involvement. Bacon mentions four: idols of the tribe, idols of the cave, idols of the marketplace, and idols of the theater.

[3] Warren O. Hagstrom, *The Scientific Community* (New York: Basic Books, 1965), p. 217.

journals and professional societies are important in maintaining high standards of research, but they are structurally weak. Ultimately, the university department, backed by the prestige and support of the university itself, accounts for the organizational strength of the autonomous system. As Hagstrom states,

> Specialized journals and scientific societies may help maintain the distinctive goals of the field, but they are highly vulnerable. The heterogeneity of the societies makes it difficult for them to form a community that can more or less monopolize recognition for work in a special area. Since they can control neither recruitment into the field nor the socialization of recruits, their goals and effectiveness may change as their composition changes. . . . we may say that a department manifests a strong commitment on the part of the university. Departments reproduce themselves by providing relatively common training for recruits stressing the distinctive goals and standards of the field. The professional members of departments cannot be easily dismissed by the university. Departments may be abandoned (or "reorganized"), but this is difficult and seldom occurs. Once universities establish departments, they are committed to them and to their continuing support.[4]

Although the university department can qualify as the structural mainstay of scientific inquiry, it is not a monolithic institution. It represents an intersection of numerous specialties and sub-specialties. For example, it is not atypical to find as many as twenty or thirty fields or subfields within a single university department. In the field of chemistry it is not unusual for the following subjects to be taught within one department: [5] analytic chemistry, organic chemistry, inorganic chemistry, physical chemistry, biochemistry, colloid chemistry, solid state chemistry, theoretical chemistry, stereochemistry of organic compounds, organic nitrogen compounds, enzymes, heterocyclic compounds, biochemistry of the nucleic acids, chemistry of the proteins, quantum chemistry, electrochemistry, chemical thermodynamics, chemical kinetics, and radio chemistry — a total of nineteen spe-

[4] *Ibid*.
[5] University of Nebraska Catalogue 1968–69.

cialties. Other departments of science are likewise characterized by proliferating teaching and research interests.

In response to this development, two questions seem appropriate: (1) Might not the pluralism inherent in scientific specialization create problems for maintaining a perception system of spontaneous self-adjustment? (2) Are most university-based scientists satisfied with the adjustment patterns of the autonomous system, or would they prefer some other model? An answer to the first question is rather difficult, since little, if any, statistical evidence is available. Scientist-administrators like Alvin Weinberg, however, assure us that the autonomous system is not organizationally strong enough to control the entropy inherent in scientific specialization. But beyond the published statements of such scientists, there is only scanty information about the impact of specialization on the coordination of scientific perceptions.[6]

---

[6] The most persistent critic of the current method of assimilating scientific information is J. D. Bernal. His original statement on the point can be found in *The Social Function of Science* (London, 1939), where he suggested that the time had come to find a more effective means of professional communication than the scientific journal. His latest essay reflects upon the earlier proposal and finds it still quite valid:

> What I had proposed in *The Social Function*, the effective supersession of the scientific journal, was strenuously opposed and was even condemned in *The Times* as an "insidious and cavalier proposal" when put to the Royal Society Conference on Scientific Information in 1947. Where I was wrong was not in the direction in which improvement would come, but in overestimating the ease with which it would happen and underestimating the prejudices that were holding it back.
> . . . The units of scientific information will have to be collected, sifted, and sorted, largely electronically, before they can be usefully presented to those who want to use them.

J. D. Bernal, "After Twenty-Five Years," in Maurice Goldsmith and Alan MacKay, eds., *The Science of Science* (Bungay, England: Pelican Books, 1966), p. 297.

For additional references to the "information crisis" within the scientific community see R. H. Phelps and J. P. Herling, "Alternatives to the Scientific Periodical," *Unesco Bulletin for Libraries* 14 (1960): 69–71; U.S. President's Science Advisory Committee, *Science, Government and Information: The Responsibilities of the Technical Community and Government in the Transfer of Information* (Washington, 1963) (Report of the Panel on Science Information) (Chairman A. M. Weinberg); K. Way, N. B. Gove,

The second question is considerably easier. In general, the answer is that the autonomous system is regarded as quite satisfactory. My own survey questionnaire contained three items that apply directly to coordination patterns that scientists might be expected to endorse. One was designed to sample feelings toward the autonomous system,[7] another to locate support for a mixed system of coordination, involving both scientific and governmental institutions,[8] and the last to measure sentiment for direct governmental supervision of scientific effort.[9] The response patterns are presented in Table 3.1.

From the sampling data it is evident that the autonomous system is preferred unequivocally by over three-quarters of the scientists who work within universities, and that the synoptic system is altogether without significant support. In contrast, the mixed system generates an ambiguous response pattern — with 35 per cent opposed, 25 per cent undecided, and 41 per cent in favor of it. If the sampling frame is stratified by age and "occupation" (Tables 3.2–3.7), the autonomous system is still clearly preferred. What little uncertainty is shown toward it is greatest between the ages of 34 and 48 (Table 3.2) and is confined largely to those in either administrative or research capacities (Table 3.5).

Generally, the mixed system is not favored by the scientific community, but it does have considerable support in certain age groups, particularly those who are 34–38, 39–43, and 45–58 (Table 3.3). In no age bracket does the mixed system receive the unqualified enthusiasm given to the autonomous system. But interestingly the mixed system is more enthusiastically supported

---

and R. van Lieshour, "Waiting for Mr. Know-it-all, or, Scientific Information Tools We Could Have Now," *Physics Today* 15 (February 1962): 22–27; Herbert Coblans, "The Communication of Information," in M. Goldsmith and A. MacKay, eds., *The Science of Science*, pp. 113–123.

[7] This system represents Polanyi's position discussed in Chapter 2.

[8] The mixed system comes closest to the model described by Don K. Price (Chapter 2).

[9] A system of direct, overhead supervision is much more extreme even than Toulmin's model of science (Chapter 2). The question was designed to see just how far toward synoptic organization scientists were willing to go. As the results show, they are not willing to go very far.

Table 3.1 PERCENTAGE RESPONSE TO THREE SYSTEMS OF SCIENTIFIC COORDINATION

Questions[a]	Type of System	Number	Strongly Agree	Agree	Can't Say	Disagree	Strongly Disagree	Total[b]
10	autonomous	835	40%	37%	7%	14%	1%	99%
14	mixed	843	5	36	25	31	4	101
17	synoptic	845	1	3	3	38	54	99

[a] Questions:

10: "The pursuit of science is best organized when as much freedom as possible is granted to all scientists."

14: "Largely because the institutions of science and government in the United States have, through interaction, evolved into a workable system of checks and balances, we have a very strong scientific and technological community."

17: "The federal government should directly supervise the activities of science so its achievements are directed to socially beneficial ends."

[b] Percentages are rounded to the nearest whole number, so some totals do not equal 100%.

Table 3.2 RESPONSE BY AGE TO THE AUTONOMOUS SYSTEM OF SCIENTIFIC COORDINATION

Age	Number	Strongly Agree	Agree	Can't Say	Disagree	Strongly Disagree	Total
23–28	70	43%	39%	7%	11%	0%	100%
29–33	133	35	41	12	12	1	101
34–38	164	35	40	6	18	1	100
39–43	104	38	33	10	16	3	100
44–48	134	37	35	6	19	2	99
49–53	61	48	33	5	13	2	101
54–58	63	46	38	8	8	0	100
59–68	76	45	41	4	11	0	101

Table 3.3 RESPONSE BY AGE TO THE MIXED SYSTEM OF SCIENTIFIC COORDINATION

Age	Number	Strongly Agree	Agree	Can't Say	Disagree	Strongly Disagree	Total
23–28	70	1%	24%	34%	37%	4%	100%
29–33	133	7	25	26	39	4	101
34–38	164	5	42	24	25	5	101
39–43	104	5	40	23	29	3	100
44–48	134	5	32	22	37	4	100
49–53	61	5	34	25	33	3	100
54–58	63	6	40	19	29	6	100
59–68	76	5	36	26	31	2	100

Table 3.4 RESPONSE BY AGE TO THE SYNOPTIC SYSTEM OF SCIENTIFIC COORDINATION

Age	Number	Strongly Agree	Agree	Can't Say	Disagree	Strongly Disagree	Total
23–28	70	0%	6%	3%	38%	54%	101%
29–33	133	3	4	2	39	52	100
34–38	164	2	3	2	38	56	101
39–43	104	1	2	4	39	55	101
44–48	134	2	2	6	47	43	100
49–53	61	3	1	3	31	63	101
54–58	63	2	4	1	31	61	99
59–63	58	4	4	4	44	44	100
64–68	18	0	3	0	31	66	100

Table 3.5 RESPONSE BY TYPE OF WORK TO THE AUTONOMOUS SYSTEM

Type of Work	Num- ber	Strongly Agree	Agree	Can't Say	Dis- agree	Strongly Disagree	Total
Adminis- trative	85	28%	43%	3%	24%	2%	100%
Research	149	31	37	10	20	2	100
Teaching- Research	561	44	36	8	10	1	99

Table 3.6 RESPONSE BY TYPE OF WORK TO THE MIXED SYSTEM

Type of Work	Num- ber	Strongly Agree	Agree	Can't Say	Dis- agree	Strongly Disagree	Total
Adminis- trative	83	7%	39%	18%	32%	3%	99%
Research	149	3	37	26	29	5	100
Teaching- Research	563	5	34	26	31	5	101

Table 3.7 RESPONSE BY TYPE OF WORK TO THE SYNOPTIC SYSTEM

Type of Work	Num- ber	Strongly Agree	Agree	Can't Say	Dis- agree	Strongly Disagree	Total
Adminis- trative	83	2%	3%	6%	38%	51%	100%
Research	149	1	3	4	37	55	100
Teaching- Research	561	2	2	4	39	54	101

by administrators than by research workers, or by those involved in teaching-research (Table 3.6). Still, it is difficult to know precisely how far those in favor of a mixed system are willing to go. The "depth" interviews suggest that opinion is divided over the extent to which government and science should interact. Some scientists want only modest governmental regulation, with scientific institutions shouldering most of the decision-making responsibility. Others want a greater degree of governmental involvement — a higher sensitivity within the scientific community to public purpose. Perhaps part of the general ambivalence stems simply from the lack of an explicitly acknowledged public policy concerning the relations between science and government.

Another possible explanation for the ambivalence shown toward a mixed system of coordination is that a university scientist usually does not think of his work as having technological consequences. When he speaks of science, he refers to "pure" research. In his research he hears, sees, and speaks no "evil." [10] But remind him of nuclear weaponry, pesticides, chemical explosives, lethal drugs, etc. – some of the devastating practical derivatives of scientific research – and he is more likely to be sympathetic to some form of outside control. Only when he visualizes science in some technological capacity does he willingly concede that the autonomous system is inadequate. Since the question concerning the "mixed system" refers to both a "scientific *and* a technological community," the ambivalent response may have been due to some confusion over which "scientific community" the question was meant to probe.

While the majority of university scientists do not resist arguments about the need for external regulation of technology, a few urge that we need be no more energetic here than in the regulation of business practice. A Nobel Laureate who maintains close ties with the technological community put the matter this way:

> Scientific technology and the technological community do not need regulation – or at least no more than what already exists in

[10] J. Bronowski's vision of the scientific virtue is instructive here:

> By the worldly standards of public life, all scholars in their work are oddly virtuous. They do not make wild claims, they do not cheat, they do not try to persuade at any cost, they appeal neither to prejudice nor to authority, they are often frank about their ignorance, their disputes are fairly decorous, they do not confuse what is being argued with race, politics, sex or age, they listen patiently to the young and to the old who both know everything. *These are the general virtues of scholarship, and they are peculiarly the virtues of science.* [emphasis mine]

Quoted from J. Bronowski's *Science and Human Values*, 1956, in Daniel S. Greenberg, *The Politics of Pure Science* (New York: The New American Library, 1967), p. 26.

the business world. They are regulated, for example, by antitrust legislation, by corporate competition, by consumer demand — all of which are very effective. Any more would appear as an excessive burden.

A much more common response is provided by an internationally famous chemist whom I interviewed at the University of Texas:

> You asked me about the scientist and social responsibility. I have definite convictions here. A pure scientist must not deny himself a discovery by worrying about social consequences. He can't possibly know the practical derivatives of his work and, therefore, cannot be held responsible for the eventual use to which his discoveries may be put. Technology, however, is different. While not separable from science, it nevertheless affects society directly and must be managed by society.

The general assumption among university-based scientists is that a spectrum of research grades from "pure" at one end to "applied" at the other. Only within the area clearly belonging to *applied* research do university scientists feel that the autonomous system should be supplemented by external controls. They do think one type of applied research, however, ought to be supervised by the highest decision-making institutions within the country: research committed to the military-industrial complex. Here is how a young mathematics professor outlined the problem:

> The American people have been led to believe, by events, by the media, and to some extent, possibly consciously by the government, that science is really a military activity, an extremely important cold-war front. The image of the scientist is that of a man involved in arcane calculations to harness unimaginably powerful sources to prevent the Soviets from harnessing them first, and thereby destroying us. Even if the scientist is engaged in basic research, he should be supported, according to popular belief, because his work may have military ramifications. And since an utterly esoteric subject produced the Bomb, the average man not only doesn't dare question the necessity for fundamental research, but only feels safe if certain esoteric subjects, such as particle physics, are well enough funded to be pursued vigorously. Nuclear fear, and its child, chemical paranoia, ex-

plain why physics and chemistry are so well funded and philosophy, which is equally esoteric, and some branches of which are equally useful commercially — for instance, modern logic is one of the keys to computer technology — is not. As far as the position of science vis-à-vis the public and the government is concerned . . . people do indeed know enough to judge the actions of their leaders, if not on a day-to-day basis, at least in the long run. But they don't believe that they do, because they ascribe more wisdom to missile scientists, generals, and executives than is warranted. *We can only divorce science and industry from the military complex if we, the American people, regain some faith in our good judgment. We must divorce science and industry from the military complex to save our nation's soul, and possibly its life!* [11]

A well-known immunologist, however, felt that while overhead democratic control of the military-industrial complex was desirable, the solution to the problem ultimately lay with the scientist himself:

Scientists qua scientists are not interested in the application of their ideas and discoveries. But they probably ought to be. For example, scientists ought to refuse to work on pathological micro-organisms because society will undoubtedly use this knowledge wrongly. There are areas of investigation where the knowledge gained can be used either for good or evil, e.g., cancer viruses, and here scientists can't make such a clear-cut choice. But there are many unambiguous areas. And I would personally like to see, say, a hundred top physicists in this country who work as consultants on atomic energy refuse to continue. Maybe this would force the government to change or modify its policy.

The assumption made thus far is that the autonomous system works in all areas of scientific research which can qualify as "pure" — an idea strongly held by university scientists. The instances they designate as proper targets for overhead democratic control are always either research projects that cost the public a lot of money or technological problems that affect almost

---

[11] These remarks and the next two extracts were written in response to the survey questionnaire.

everyone. A chemist and member of the National Academy of Sciences tried to clarify the matter in the following way:

> Scientists engaged in pure research should in no way be controlled unless that research requires the outlay of funds from larger society in a substantial way. Projects which demand heavy funding must rely on the decision-making machinery of society to determine whether they should be undertaken. Of course, it helps immensely if you have an enlightened society, but, in any event, you must take your chances with this larger body. Sometimes if you are personally interested in a project, you may enlist the services of your peers and colleagues and this may enhance its chances of success. But basically the problem is that of society.
>
> It is perhaps impossible to make a hard and fast distinction between pure science and technology. Yet it is surely the latter that is apparent in the lives of most Americans. I would insist, however, that no area of investigation be closed because someone feels that society is incapable of handling it. The responsibility for the proper use of technological achievement is fundamentally social and moral, not scientific (e.g., should television become "Big Brother," should we make nuclear bombs, should we make the desert bloom?).

In the abstract, then, this well-known chemist could argue that the line between "pure" and "applied" research is always fine and frequently indistinct. But when asked to classify his own research, he laughed and said, "Why, pure, of course." Perhaps not unwittingly, this remark shows how delicate the whole issue of applied research is within universities. It is simply not considered good form to embrace it. There is also a deeper reason: applied research has built-in handicaps because of its potential threat to the autonomous system. Since there is general agreement that society has a right to regulate technology, university scientists in justifying professional autonomy tend to regard applied science as a "negative commodity." They do not, however, explicitly condemn scientific applications — in the popular mind that might come close to censuring pure science itself. Rather, they define applied research as a second-rate enterprise incapable of developing new ideas and principles on its own. Harvard chemist George

B. Kistiakowsky carefully summarized the argument for Congress:

> The point that requires repeated emphasis is that closely defined
> mission-oriented research, another term for applied research, has
> value, but, by itself, is insufficient and incapable of developing
> really new ideas and new principles on which each practical
> mission will ultimately find itself based. If the social climate and
> support mechanisms are not such as to encourage the free ex-
> ploration of new ideas rapidly and effectively, our technology
> will die on the vine, because in the absence of the results of
> new, undirected basic research, applied work tends to become
> more and more confined to increasingly expensive refinements of
> and elaborations of old ideas.[12]

Kistiakowsky's appeal is characteristic of academic testimony
before public bodies, but off the record, university scientists are
less sure of themselves. And well they might be, for Daniel
Greenberg has shown that

> as often as not, the history of science and technology fails to
> conform to the pure scientists' tidy model of science as the
> father of technology. It would be convenient, for example, if a
> comprehension of thermodynamics had paved the way to the
> creation of the steam engine, but, if anything, it appears that
> the steam engine paved the way to a comprehension of thermo-
> dynamics — and the inspiration for this effort at comprehension
> was a desire for a still more efficient steam engine. Which came
> first, which was of greater importance, the science or the tech-
> nology? Upon close examination, it becomes clear that these are
> the wrong questions; that rather than a straight-line sequence
> from knowledge to utility, there has prevailed an interaction of
> such incredibly complex and intricate composition that it is
> rarely possible in examining any artifact or device to sift the
> science from the technology.[13]

[12] Quoted in Greenberg, *The Politics of Pure Science*, pp. 28–29.
[13] *Ibid.*, p. 29. See also Richard R. Nelson, "The Economics of Invention:
A Survey of the Literature," *Journal of Business*, April 1959; Charles H.
Townes, "Quantum Electronics, and Surprise in Development of Technology," *Science* 159, no. 3816 (February 16, 1968): 699–710.

Although the distinction between pure and applied research is a matter of great complexity, scientists should not be condemned for making it. One simply should be made aware of the *social function* of the distinction. Pure science is differentiated from technology or applied research in order to preserve the spatial dimensions of the autonomous system. The majority of pure scientists are not knowingly pompous or deceitful; rather they feel the autonomous system can provide a more reliable articulation of the purposes of science and its epistemic commitments. The adjustment patterns that thrive under the protection of autonomy stimulate a style of scientific imagination (a "vision") which might not be possible if its social and political space were enlarged. Applied research almost automatically means that the spatial dimensions of science must be stretched to accommodate a new variety of individuals and institutions affected by the work. This tendency, if accelerated, might ultimately mean that the autonomous system would lose its power to define the objectives as well as the "growing points" of scientific research.

The stress placed upon the spatial dimension of the autonomous system comes from two directions. From without, the demand is that science become a part of the industrial and technological complex — and thus lend its resources to the achievement of practical and political objectives in the community at large. From within, the pressure is epitomized by the criticism that university departments have an ideological bias against a technical or applied curriculum — a curriculum that is intrinsically as rewarding and innovative as pure science. Three responses to the survey questionnaire illustrate these themes. The first two come from scientists employed by E. I. Du Pont De Nemours & Co.,[14] emphasizing the first proposition; the third from an ecologist at a lower-ranked university, stressing the second.

I regard question ten [which dealt with interest in the autonomous system] as ambiguous, even highly ambiguous. I think

[14] Before I discovered that lack of funds and clerical assistance would eventually reduce the sampling universe, I mailed out around 150 posttest questionnaires to Du Pont. The two responses here are from this group.

that a scientist should have freedom to choose his own route to the solution of problems, but freedom (implying support) to study anything without regard to probable value to society (government, business, people-at-large) seems to me to be not only unlikely, but undesirable.

I feel that as society becomes more technological, the motivation of political power will assume a greater importance to scientists as contrasted with their history of antipolitical sentiments. This above trend is already apparent.

I feel that science is meant to serve many ends, of which the search for absolute truth and new knowledge is important, but not the only objective. The training, methods, and factual knowledge gained by scientists need to be employed also in those areas of public need. In other words, the application of scientific knowledge is, to me, as important as the gaining of new scientific knowledge. *I have the definite feeling that in my own discipline applied science is denigrated consistently by the academic and teaching components of the field.*

The values and institutions presently associated with scientific work are those of the autonomous system. But there is increasing tension between demands imposed by the structures of "autonomous space" and the new institutions of technology that are emerging. Many scientists seem trapped by these developments. Their primary loyalty is to the values of the autonomous system, but they are very much aware of the external forces bearing down upon it. Scientists at lower-ranked institutions are the first to feel these tensions, for at this level there is not enough organizational strength and institutional wealth to provide much insulation from external pressures. A geologist at one of these universities described the condition clearly:

I think most sociologists studying the sociology of science are missing the central issue, in part because the changes in the structure of science have been so rapid and so fundamental. In the last eight years, grantsmanship has become the central phenomenon in the sociology of science.

At this moment relatively small groups of people influence the distribution of large grants for scientific research. Unfortunately this means that they decide in large part what lines of scientific investigation will be pursued, what methods will be employed and who will do the work.

As a result, freedom of investigation has become a joke. Most scientists are in a position of being free to investigate anything that they can get the money to investigate, which means that they investigate the things that are favored by the influential, or investigate nothing.

Science was unique, and could be uniquely structured because it was independent of "this year's budget" or "next month's balance sheet," but this is no longer true. In 8 or 10 years' time, science has been restructured as a profit-making industry, and the negative effects on general scientific work have already begun to show.

Whether these external conditions will succeed completely or only partially in restructuring science is a matter of conjecture. But in the interim, although under stress, the autonomous system lingers. One of the reasons for this, no doubt, is the effectiveness of its social norms, for even those who think that the autonomous system is inadequate do not fault the entire panel of norms that regulate its roles and reward its practitioners. This issue should now be considered.

THE SOCIAL NORMS OF SCIENTIFIC RESEARCH

The autonomy of science leads to a set of commonly held expectations about how scientists should conduct their research. These values or norms, according to Merton, "define technically and morally allowable patterns of behavior, indicating what is prescribed, preferred, permitted, or proscribed." [15] They therefore serve to protect the interests of the individual scientist and to preserve the social relations of the autonomous system. Without their presence the autonomous system would become an indistinct dimension of social space; and scientific conflicts might thus become matters for macropolitical resolution or else the substance of purely individual disputes.

By stabilizing behavior expectations, the norms of science create conditions under which the interactions of scientists can

---

[15] Robert K. Merton, "The Ambivalence of Scientists," in Norman Kaplan, ed., *Science and Society* (Chicago: Rand McNally, 1965), p. 112.

actually contribute to the perceptive qualities of scientific inquiry. They reduce the uncertainties of interpersonal frictions to a level of tolerance that enables the "politics of science" to function as a *sensor* to the observable world.

As already indicated, the spatial dimensions of the autonomous system are under continuous stress. This judgment should surprise no one, for all areas of social and political space must be constantly affirmed against the entropy of an "environment" — whether, for example, the activity involves the clarification of powers between a central government and a state in a federal system or simply the right of a family, as opposed to the local school, to instruct its children on morals.

Within the scientific community a perpetual struggle goes on against outside demands for institutional change. While the impact of these pressures is seldom directly visible, an indication of their presence is reflected in shifting attitudes toward norms of inquiry. Thus, a convenient hypothesis emerges: when the conventional norms of science are either rejected completely or when they are ambiguously regarded, there is reason to believe that the traditional boundaries of research are in a state of adjustment.

If the spatial viability of the autonomous system is to be assessed fully, something must be known of its social norms and their general reception by scientists. The literature on the sociology of science systematically characterizes the autonomous system as responding to seven norms that regulate its social interaction: (1) universalism, (2) communism, (3) disinterestedness, (4) organized skepticism, (5) rationality, (6) emotional neutrality, and (7) individualism. The first four are suggested by Robert Merton, whose early essay on the subject is still the most persuasive effort to conceptualize the social dimensions of scientific inquiry.[16] The last three are found in Bernard Barber's *Science and the Social Order*.[17] It will soon become obvious, how-

[16] Robert K. Merton, "Science and Democratic Social Structure," *Social Theory and Social Structure* (Glencoe, Ill.: The Free Press, 1949), pp. 309–316.

[17] Bernard Barber, *Science and the Social Order* (Glencoe, Ill.: The Free Press, 1952), pp. 84–88.

ever, that it is difficult, if not impossible, to maintain clear lines of distinction among all the norms at selected levels of empirical analysis. But in general, the following definitions do justice to the literature:

Universalism — The realization that all scientists are obligated to uphold common, objective standards of truth that transcend personal influence or social position.

Communism — The recognition that effective communication is essential to science and that "property rights" have no place in the dissemination of scientific findings.

Disinterestedness — Disavowal of personal or material interest in the product of scientific research.

Organized Skepticism — Acceptance of the idea that each scientist is responsible for critically evaluating the work of his peers and for suspending his judgment until "the facts are at hand."

Rationality — Adherence to objective, consensual standards of proof.

Emotional Neutrality — A prohibition against intense personal commitment to particular ideas or theories to the extent that their truth or falsity might be affected.

Individualism — Commitment to resist any regulation or control of scientific research.

In regulating the mood and expectation of conflict, the norms of science serve as collecting points for generalized opinions. They help designate not only what kind of "scientific" behavior is appropriate, but in many instances how it should be expressed. In this fashion, the overall contour of the norms of science bears an unmistakable resemblance to what David Truman has called "the rules of the game" — a phrase which refers to "widely held, unorganized interests within the community." [18] Moreover, Truman emphasizes that when the "rules of the game" are "violated," the political space in which they are operative becomes indistinct, that is, loses its *cohesion*. Although Truman uses the expres-

[18] David B. Truman, *The Governmental Process* (New York: Alfred A. Knopf, 8th printing, 1962), p. 512.

sion "group" to designate political space, his meaning is unmistakably clear:

> Violation of "the rules of the game" normally will weaken a group's cohesion, reduce its status in the community, and expose it to the claims of other groups. The latter may be competing organized groups that more adequately incorporate the "rules," or they may be groups organized on the basis of these broad interests and in response to the violations.[19]

To understand how the norms of science function, one need only recall the "Velikovsky affair." While the details of the episode are beyond the scope of this account, it is illuminating to analyze the reactions of scientists to something they regarded as a violation of proper scientific behavior. In 1950 Immanuel Velikovsky published a book called *Worlds in Collision*, in which he argued that our present solar system is the product of cosmic cataclysms involving collisions between major planets. He supported this idea, not just by extrapolations from "accepted theories of mechanics . . . electricity and magnetism," [20] but by records of ancient eclipses and by numerous historical myths and folktales concerning cosmic disturbances. Leading scientists regarded this approach as fundamentally wrong and therefore unsuited either for debate or further theoretical study. So in order to make his case, Velikovsky went beyond the critical scrutiny of the scientific community and presented his findings directly to the public.

As a result, scientists throughout the United States were outraged, for Velikovsky appeared to flaunt the traditional commitment to *disinterestedness*. Opinions of scientists began to coalesce around that issue, until finally, through threat of economic boycott, the original publisher of Velikovsky's book was forced to abandon publication. A prominent magazine editor and a well-known museum director lost their jobs because they refused to

19 *Ibid.*
20 From astronomer Lloyd Motz's letter to *Harper's* 227, no. 1361 (October 1963): 12.

repudiate Velikovsky's position.[21] Popular journals and magazines were flooded with letters and articles written by scientists exposing Velikovsky's "fraudulent" theory, many legitimately questioning his use of "historical" data as scientific evidence. But the central source of concern seemed to be that Velikovsky's ideas were generating widespread enthusiasm — without first having been qualified by reputable scientific opinion. Two samples of this criticism appear below.

The editors of *Science* noted at the bottom of a letter which had compared Velikovsky's *Worlds in Collision* to Grimm's fairy tales and the *Rubaiyat:*

> [We] have been only too mindful of the box-office successes and best-seller records of plays and books that have been literary and financial failures until some society, watchful of public morals, gave them the boost that paid off. There is, however, cause for alarm that there are publishers and editors [who favor Velikovsky] so scientifically illiterate as to appear unable to differentiate between fact and fiction — authentic science and hoax.[22]

Geochemist Harrison Brown, in reviewing Velikovsky's second book, *Earth in Upheaval* (1956), outlined the professionally acceptable way for a scientist to present new evidence, and then speculated about why Velikovsky's first book met such determined resistance from the scientific community:

> In the world of science the individual research worker usually subjects his results and theories to his fellow scientists for searching criticism and checking before making his results known to the public. If he is at a university he first solicits the criticisms of his local colleagues, following which he shows his results to scientists in other institutions. When he has thus satisfied himself that his results or ideas make sense, he submits a paper to a scientific journal. The paper is sent to anonymous referees for criticism, and if they judge it worth publishing it is published in that journal.

[21] An account of these events may be found in Alfred de Grazia, *et al.*, eds., *The Velikovsky Affair* (New York: University Books, 1966).

[22] *Science* 114, no. 2950 (July 13, 1951): 47.

The strong feelings expressed by scientists following the publication of *Worlds in Collision* stemmed in large part from the fact that an inordinate amount . . . of credence had been given to the theory by magazines, newspapers and the book's publishers without any attempt being made to ask whether or not the theory made sense. The discipline normally imposed by scientists upon themselves had been bypassed.[23]

The present suggestion is not that the scientists who opposed Velikovsky were blindly prejudiced to all views except their own, but rather that the norms of scientific inquiry can actually mold unorganized interests within the scientific community. Yet in general, response patterns to professional "crises" are not commonly so unequivocal as they might seem from the Velikovsky controversy. Sometimes scientists are confronted by indistinct norms, or norms that are tenuously regarded, and less certain action follows. Under these conditions some norms assume qualities of ambiguity, that is, they generate responses that neither affirm nor deny their importance to inquiry.

Ambiguous norms, however, may be indicators of changes taking place within the social and political space where they operate. For their presence prevents the effective conversion of unorganized sentiment (or opinion) into organized activity in order that the spatial dimensions in question may be preserved. It is, of course, unlikely that any dimension of political space will be completely free from ambiguity. But the degree to which it is, gives evidence of institutional cohesion and clarity of purpose.

Although the state of normative ambiguity may directly affect the political process, there is not a single published survey that tries to measure its presence within the autonomous system of science. Perhaps researchers are too prudent to commit themselves to such an ambitious and open-ended assignment. But the norms of science are no less general and no more difficult to explore than, say, the norms of political "conservatism," and the latter are canvassed without hesitation.[24]

---

[23] *Scientific American* 194, no. 3 (March 1956): 127–128.
[24] For example, see T. W. Adorno, *et al.*, *The Authoritarian Personality* (New York: Harper, 1950); H. McClosky, "Conservatism and Personality,"

The questionnaire used in this study attempts to supply new information about the condition of normative ambiguity within the autonomous system. In order to obtain that data, several questions were chosen that covered referents for each norm (see Table 3.8). When the results were analyzed, two types of ambiguity became apparent. Type I relates to contradictory positions taken on alternate referents of the same norm; type II involves an uncertain response to a single referent. In each case response patterns were considered decisive (or unambiguous) when the percentage margin between "agree" and "disagree" was above 8 per cent. Perhaps this figure carries a conservative bias, but until more precise techniques are available and further studies conducted, it is sufficient to indicate those areas in which ambiguity is not likely to exist; and by contrast, restrictive enough to provide focus for opinions, beneath this percentage, that do reveal ambiguous tendencies.

Only one norm, universalism, qualifies for consideration under the first type of ambiguity. Its content is orientational rather than directive in purpose,[25] and while it commands wide generalized respect, at the level of day-to-day scientific work it has little, if any, operational effectiveness. This may be seen by looking at Table 3.8. The questions (numbers 25 and 29 respectively) designed to prove the generalized claim that standards of scientific truth are universally governed by pre-established impersonal criteria were each answered in the affirmative. But the question (number 22) that tried to explore the working significance of the norm by asking whether one's social position influenced the acceptance or rejection of scientific evidence was answered in such a way as to contradict the two previous responses. Perhaps a partial explanation for this is that scientists within the autonomous

---

American Political Science Review 52 (1958): 27–45; M. Rokeach, *The Open and the Closed Mind* (New York: Basic Books, 1960); B. Anderson, *et al.,* "On Conservative Attitudes," *Acta Sociologica* 8 (1965): 188–204; and Robert A. Schoenberger, "Conservatism, Personality, and Political Extremism," *American Political Science Review* 62 (1968): 868–877.

[25] Norman Storer, *The Social System of Science* (New York: Holt, Rinehart & Winston, 1966), p. 78.

Table 3.8   AGREEMENT AND DISAGREEMENT ON THE NORMS OF SCIENTIFIC RESEARCH

Norm	Questions	Number	Percentage Response			Total
			Agree	Disagree	Undecided	
Universalism	22: "The acceptance or nonacceptance of scientific evidence does not in any way depend upon the social position of the one who submits it (that is, his institutional affiliation – university or lab – his degree of recognition, those under whom he has studied or worked)."	840	33	60	7	100
	25: "Scientists must adhere to a common set of objective standards by which proof can be demonstrated."	832	64	29	7	100
	29: "Despite different cultural backgrounds and different patterns of belief, scientists (all over the world) can communicate effectively with each other because the terms used for communication have precisely the same meaning to the various members of the scientific community".	838	72	22	6	100
Communism	1: "For science to be advanced it is not enough that fruitful ideas be originated, or new experiments developed, or new methods instituted; the innovations must be effectively *communicated* to others."	849	97	1	1	99

Norm	Statement	No.				Total
	21: "Only those scientists who have high standing, or work or associate informally with those who do, have the kind of information that lies at the cutting edge of inquiry."	831	30	57	12	99
	30: "In the area of fundamental research, scientists regard their ideas as common property; they regard suppression of information or scientific discoveries (providing, say national security is not threatened) as unethical."	842	82	12	6	100
Disinterestedness	31: "Science differs from other professions (medicine, law, etc.) in that there is less chance that a scientist would take advantage (financial or otherwise) of the layman."	818	47	30	23	100
Organized Skepticism	32: "Scientists are skeptical even about their own findings until other scientists have evaluated them."	819	44	45	11	100
Rationality	25: "Scientists must adhere to a common set of objective standards by which proof may be demonstrated."	832	64	29	7	100
Emotional Neutrality	24: "Intense personal commitment to ideas or theories is not a proper scientific attitude."	834	42	50	8	100
Individualism	10: "The pursuit of science is best organized when as much freedom as possible is granted to all scientists."	835	77	15	7	99

system collectively share many of the same characteristics of the citizenry as a whole. Herbert McClosky, for example, discovered that the orientation norm *freedom* was abstractly associated by the electorate with democracy. But when practical, issue-oriented referents were devised to further test the attitude, he found that opinions divided sharply.[26] Like the electorate, scientists can respond with a decisive commitment to a norm of generalized or abstract significance, but radically withdraw their loyalty when its content becomes more direct and personal. Universalism seems to be characterized by this response pattern.

The second type of ambiguity is represented by the norms of *organized skepticism* and *emotional neutrality*. Responses to both norms indicate that there is a significant degree of uncertainty with respect to their application in the research process of science. The basic concern is with the proper role of personality in research. Personality has an important influence upon the degree of commitment and the intensity of effort that accompany serious scientific work. Scientists are particularly sensitive as individuals to the prospects of selecting their own research problems, choosing the methods and techniques that seem appropriate to them, and evaluating the results without "overhead" supervision.[27] Yet the autonomous system tries to prevent the emergence of "self-generated rewards" as the foundation of scientific research.[28] The reason for this is quite clear: unless there is some restraint against idiosyncratic behavior, the quality of scientific perception is thrown open to question, and the institutions of science that have focused the activity begin to blur in purpose and cohesiveness.

The ambiguity generated by organized skepticism and emotional neutrality may indicate a challenge to the spatial characteristics of pure research. This alone, of course, does not mean that the autonomous system is to be reshaped suddenly, or that the internal tensions with which it has to cope are too powerful to be accommodated. But it does imply a potential unsteadiness that could manifest itself under conditions of severe stress. The autonomous system must therefore not be taken for granted if it is to

26 H. McClosky, "Consensus and Ideology in American Politics," *American Political Science Review* 58 (1964): 373.

27 Hagstrom, *The Scientific Community*, p. 105.

28 Storer, *The Social System of Science*, p. 116.

survive as a cohesive dimension of political space. In fact, the "politics of pure science" should routinely involve monitoring feelings of normative ambiguity as a partial gauge to the actual capacity of the system.

To suggest that normative ambivalence may affect the "shape" of political space is only to affirm the conditions that are requisite for the latter's existence. As Wolin has pointed out, political space depends upon the development of a distinctive consciousness — an awareness that particular structural relations exist and persist. Moreover, as he insists, there must also be "internal" arrangements within this designated area for resolving the tensions that grow out of a sense of common preoccupation and involvement.[29] Normative ambiguity is a negative function of both of these requirements. It blurs spatial boundaries and decreases confidence in "internal" expectations for settling disputes and resolving conflict.

In this respect, the ambiguity represented by organized skepticism and emotional neutrality is more demoralizing than the type associated with universalism, for it reveals a much more puzzling, more astonishing confusion. The type of ambiguity to which universalism belongs (type I) refers to the coexistence of antithetical attitudes toward a given norm. Yet only one attitude at a time emerges into consciousness; the other remains unconscious. In contrast, the ambiguity created by organized skepticism and emotional neutrality (type II) points to an almost simultaneous awareness of antithetical attitudes — a condition that may well be a variant to anomic behavior.

The possibility of a parallel between this form of ambiguity and patterns of anomic behavior cannot yet be demonstrated with evidence, but it nevertheless deserves comment. The general assumption is that anomic feelings create the impression that the spatial dimensions of one's life or work are no longer meaningful, no longer powerful enough to hold back an undifferentiated environment. Norms that have previously guided conduct — by serving to settle conflict and allay anxieties — become indefinite and remote. The focus of one's activities begins to blur into a bewil-

[29] Sheldon S. Wolin, *Politics and Vision* (Boston: Little, Brown, 1960), p. 16.

dering sense of directionlessness. The conventional explanation for this development is that social or cultural barriers build until individuals are driven to deviant action. As Merton urges, anomie represents "a breakdown in the cultural structure, occurring particularly when there is an acute disjunction between the cultural norms and goals and the socially structured capacities of members of the group to act in accord with them. . . . When the cultural and the social structure are malintegrated, the first calling for behavior and attitudes which the second precludes, there is a strain toward the breakdown of the norms, toward normlessness." [30]

According to this view, anomic attitudes are derived from social circumstances (particularly institutions) that deprive one from achieving the goals and purposes of his culture. In fact, a small number of *consensus* studies supports this assumption. As McClosky and Schaar indicate,

> These studies have uniformly found that the values usually considered fundamental to our way of life (e.g., belief in freedom, democracy, constitutional and procedural rights, tolerance, human dignity) are shared more widely and held more strongly among people in positions of leadership, influence, and high status than among the less favored classes. Conversely, those who occupy social positions remote from the mainstream exhibit a high incidence and intensity of anomic feelings. Because of poverty, or little education, or the conditions of their employment or residence, these people are relatively isolated from the cultural mainstream. This condition reduces . . . their ability to learn the norms of the larger community which, in turn, gives rise to feelings of normlessness.[31]

[30] Robert K. Merton, *Social Theory and Social Structure*, rev. ed. (Glencoe, Ill.: The Free Press, 1957), pp. 162–163.

[31] Herbert McClosky and John H. Schaar, "Psychological Dimensions of Anomy," *American Sociological Review* 30 (February 1965): 20. The consensus studies mentioned by these authors as representative are: Samuel A. Stouffer, *Communism, Conformity, and Civil Liberties* (New York: Doubleday, 1955); James W. Prothro and Charles M. Grigg, "Fundamental Principles of Democracy: Bases of Agreement and Disagreement," *Journal of Politics* 21 (1960): 276–294; Seymour Martin Lipset, *Political Man* (New York: Doubleday, 1960), Chap. 4; and Herbert McClosky, "Consensus and Ideology in American Politics," *American Political Science Review* 58 (June 1964): 361–382.

But McClosky and Schaar also argue that sociological determinants can only partially account for anomie as a general phenomenon. Other determinants, such as those that are cultural or deeply psychological and personal, must be considered as well. For if this were not the case, "we would expect all persons in a given role or social setting to be anomic. But this is clearly not the fact." [32] The study revealed here suggests that sociological determinants have only modest explanatory value in accounting for ambiguous attitudes within pure science — especially the type that may have anomic overtones. As Appendix Figures C.1–C.12 show, reaction to questions that (together with requested "background" data) were expressly designed to test sociological determinants failed to yield definitive results. Consequently, before further inferences can be drawn concerning the relation of normative ambiguity and anomic behavior, the scientific community must be psychologically probed — a prospect that lies beyond this study.

Although sociological factors may not supply final answers to questions about normative ambiguity (including its anomic possibilities), they may not be insignificant as contributors. This attempt, however, is only a beginning — one that cautiously prepares the way for further work by seeking to explore the broadest and most obvious sociological categories. Still, when attitudes toward organized skepticism and emotional neutrality are broken down into response by institution, discipline, age, and type of work, relationships begin to emerge that are both unexpected and revealing. The following hypotheses and tables provide the necessary organization for clarifying this information and making it relevant to the pattern of ambiguity (type II) just discussed.

Ambiguity Patterns (Type II).

1. *Institutional Influence*

HYPOTHESIS (1): Established schools of high prestige, because they are the mainstay of the autonomous system, will be more

---

[32] McClosky and Schaar, "Psychological Dimensions of Anomy," p. 20.

inclined to endorse organized skepticism and emotional neutrality than institutions of low or medium prestige.

Within the limits of the survey, this hypothesis is without adequate support (see Appendix Figures C.13–C.14). In fact, normative ambiguity toward organized skepticism is closely associated with three institutions of high prestige and just two of low prestige (see Table 3.9), while ambiguous responses to emotional neutrality characterize two institutions of high prestige and only one of low prestige (see Table 3.10). Thus, ambiguity would appear to be neither a positive nor a negative function of institutional prominence.

2. *Disciplinary Influence*

HYPOTHESIS (2): High-prestige disciplines (that is, those with tightly developed theories and well-established subject matters) are more likely to support organized skepticism and emotional neutrality than low-prestige disciplines.

Although not all scientists are inclined to give the same prestige order for each area of study, it is common within the *formal* sciences to rank mathematics first, statistics second, and logic third. One must remember, however, that the formal sciences are not empirically based, even though they provide the standards of logical precision for the other sciences.[33] Within the empirical sciences the general order of prestige is physics, chemistry, and biology, while in the observational-empirical sciences, astronomy is considered more prestigious than geology. Using this prestige scale, the survey evidence for organized skepticism and emotional neutrality consistently supports the hypothesis in only one discipline, astronomy (see Tables 3.11 and 3.12 and Appendix Figures C.15 and C.16). Physics confirms the hypothesis for organized skepticism, but rejects it on emotional neutrality. Chemistry clearly dismisses the importance of both norms, suggesting, perhaps, that an empirical discipline of high intermediate prestige may reflect normative commitments altogether different from those anticipated by the hypothesis. Biology is the only discipline

---

[33] Hagstrom, *The Scientific Community*, p. 74.

Table 3.9   REACTION BY INSTITUTION TO ORGANIZED SKEPTICISM [a]

	Clearly Reject	*Ambiguous*	*Clearly Support*
High Prestige	Princeton University	University of California (Berkeley) Stanford University California Institute of Technology	Harvard University
Medium Prestige	Washington University (St. Louis)		
Low Prestige		University of Nebraska (Lincoln) University of Idaho (Moscow)	University of Arizona (Tucson) University of Georgia (Athens)

[a] For actual percentages see Appendix Figure C.13.

Table 3.10   REACTION BY INSTITUTION TO EMOTIONAL NEUTRALITY [a]

	Clearly Reject	*Ambiguous*	*Clearly Support*
High Prestige	Harvard University University of California (Berkeley) Princeton University	Stanford University California Institute of Technology	
Medium Prestige	Washington University (St. Louis)		
Low Prestige	University of Arizona (Tucson) University of Georgia (Athens)	University of Nebraska (Lincoln)	University of Idaho (Moscow)

[a] For actual percentages see Appendix Figure C.14.

Table 3.11　Reaction by Discipline to Organized Skepticism [a]

	Rank	Clearly Reject	Ambiguous	Clearly Support
Formal Sciences[b]	High Prestige		Mathematics	
Empirical Sciences	High Prestige			Physics
	High Intermediate Prestige	Chemistry		
	Low Intermediate Prestige			Biology
Observational-Empirical Sciences	High Prestige			Astronomy
	Low Prestige			Geology

[a] For actual percentages see Appendix Figure C.15.
[b] Mathematics was the only formal science surveyed.

Table 3.12　Reaction by Discipline to Emotional Neutrality [a]

	Rank	Clearly Reject	Ambiguous	Clearly Support
Formal Sciences[b]	High Prestige	Mathematics		
Empirical Sciences	High Prestige	Physics		
	High Intermediate Prestige	Chemistry		
	Low Intermediate Prestige		Biology	
Observational-Empirical Sciences	High Prestige			Astronomy
	Low Prestige		Geology	

[a] For actual percentages see Appendix Figure C.16.
[b] Mathematics was the only formal science surveyed.

with ambiguous attitudes toward both norms, while geology responds ambiguously to emotional neutrality, but positively supports organized skepticism.

The available data do not suggest an unqualified endorsement of the idea that patterns of ambiguity linked to organized skepticism and emotional neutrality derive from matters of disciplinary prestige. Yet when each discipline is examined from the standpoint of the prevalence and severity of competition within it, new factors related to prestige emerge that deserve attention.

Competition within disciplines, according to Hagstrom, "results when scientists can agree on the relative importance of scientific problems and when many of them are able to solve these problems." [34] From this perspective, the prevalence of competition is determined by the likelihood that a scientist will be anticipated in his research, whereas severity of competition is analyzed as a consequence of anticipation. Thus, if being anticipated means that a scientist is unable to achieve recognition for his work, competition is considered severe.[35]

Using these distinctions, one may hypothesize that disciplines of high prestige will be characterized by wider prevalence and greater severity of competition than those of low prestige. The test that Hagstrom uses to shed light on this assumption was designed to demonstrate the prevalence of competition by identifying those scientists who actually experienced anticipation in their respective disciplines. Severity of competition was determined by exploring the degree to which scientists felt concerned about being anticipated. The results of both probes are illustrated by Tables 3.13 and 3.14.

On the basis of this evidence, Hagstrom concludes that the prevalence of competition is always high in disciplines that have well-integrated theories and clearly defined focuses of research. In these areas (particularly in physics) it is possible to agree in advance on which problems are the most important and where greatest recognition will come for competent results.[36] Mathematics, however, is different. Even though it can qualify as a

[34] *Ibid.*, p. 73.
[35] *Ibid.*, p. 70.
[36] *Ibid.*, p. 78.

Table 3.13   Experience of Anticipation by Scientific Field

Area	Percentage Having Been Anticipated	Number of Cases
Physical scientists	70	27
Molecular biologists	64	11
Formal scientists	48	25

Source: W. O. Hagstrom, *The Scientific Community* (New York: Basic Books, 1965), p. 75.

Table 3.14   Concern about Anticipation by Scientific Field

Area	Percentage Expressing Concern	Number of Cases
Formal scientists	61	23
Molecular biologists	55	11
Physical scientists	40	25

Source: Same as Table 3.13.

rigorously systematic field of study, its competition is less prevalent "because of the absence of agreement on the relative importance of mathematical problems." As Hagstrom indicates,

> The mathematician has great freedom, since experience cannot contradict his results. An infinite number of mathematical systems are possible and can be constructed, and the criteria for calling some of the systems more important than others, and hence some problems more important than others, are vague and not compelling. This is especially so when mathematicians spurn the criteria of practical utility, as they now do in the United States. It is often relatively difficult, therefore, for mathematicians to order problem areas in their field either according to relative importance or according to the recognition that should be awarded discoveries in them. For this reason, the prevalence of competition in mathematics can be expected to be relatively low.[37]

Unlike mathematics, molecular biology does not have a well-defined theoretical structure. At the same time there is more

[37] *Ibid.*, p. 74.

agreement in this field on what constitutes a significant research problem than in mathematics. For this reason the prevalence of competition is higher in molecular biology, and the severity of competition is lower — due to the comparative lack of precision in biological research.

If the foregoing analysis is applied to the broader survey (see Table 3.15), it appears that disciplinary prestige and competition have only marginal influence upon ambiguous attitudes toward organized skepticism and emotional neutrality. What impact there is occurs within empirical sciences of low intermediate and low prestige (biology and geology) and within the formal sciences of high prestige (mathematics). Other factors, of course, are likely to be at work here, but what they are and how they combine with prestige and competition to produce ambiguous responses await further study.

3. *Age Characteristics*

HYPOTHESIS (3): If the autonomous system is working properly, the age at which maximum scientific creativity is reached will represent a period when organized skepticism and emotional neutrality are positively affirmed.

Designating the years of maximum scientific creativity is no longer a matter of guesswork or scholarly intuition. Lehman's study of scientific fields has given statistical evidence for the age levels at which the most creative work has been done.[38] These findings indicate that in all scientific disciplines the most outstanding research is accomplished between the ages of 26 and 39. For chemistry the achievement interval is 26 to 30, for mathematics and physics 30 to 34, and for biology, geology, and astronomy 35 to 39. If this information is compared with the results of our survey, the above hypothesis is unable to explain the ambiguous attitudes expressed toward organized skepticism and emotional neutrality (see Appendix Figures C.17–C.18). Perhaps the reason for this response is that the interval of high

[38] See H. C. Lehman, *Age and Achievement* (Princeton: Princeton University Press, 1953), p. 324.

Table 3.15 IMPACT OF DISCIPLINARY PRESTIGE AND FACTORS OF COMPETITION
ON ORGANIZED SKEPTICISM AND EMOTIONAL NEUTRALITY

Prevalence of Competition	Severity of Competition				
	High	Medium high	Medium	Medium low	Low
Low	Math (high prestige; ambiguous attitude expressed toward organized skepticism)				
Medium low				Geology (low prestige; ambiguous attitude expressed toward emotional neutrality)	
Medium			Biology (low intermediate prestige; ambiguous attitude expressed toward organized skepticism and emotional neutrality)		
Medium high		Chemistry (intermediate prestige; unambiguous attitudes expressed)			
High	Physics (high prestige; unambiguous attitudes expressed) Astronomy (high prestige; unambiguous attitudes expressed)				

scientific creativity in all fields represents a period both of great individual confidence and uncertainty — a sense of excitement in challenging an accepted idea or moving beyond known frontiers and yet a fear of going too far. These paradoxical emotions are skillfully brought into focus by Gerhart Wiebe:

> For a scientist or an artist, the integrity of his self-image is closely identified with the integrity of the training and knowledge from which he derives his status as a professional. Then creative insight, which is a break with the old, is correspondingly a threat to the self-image. The tighter and more constricting the ego defenses, the more threatening would the creative insight be. The second, quiescent, part of the Incubation stage, during which creative people often report that they forget all about the problem, may then be somewhat analogous to the stage of secret diplomacy in which, the decision having been made as to what must be done if anything is to be done, the long search begins for an acceptable way of doing it. Perhaps many creative ideas die aborning because the psychological commitment to security within the *status quo* precludes the discovery, at an unconscious level, of an acceptable way for the idea to come into consciousness.[39]

Very likely there are other, more fundamental interpretations to be made of this data. Still, if all age clusters are examined carefully, the reaction to organized skepticism and emotional neutrality is surprisingly erratic. Why this happens is not clear, and until further studies are made, the effect of age upon normative ambiguity (type II) will remain problematic.

4. *Job Type and Ambiguity*

HYPOTHESIS (4): Those whose positions directly support the institutional structure of the autonomous system are less likely to express ambiguous attitudes toward emotional neutrality and organized skepticism than those whose positions only indirectly support it.

In order to reduce this assumption to operational significance, the autonomous system was divided into three "occupational"

[39] Gerhart D. Wiebe, "An Exploration into the Nature of Creativity," *Public Opinion Quarterly* 26 (Fall 1962): 394.

categories: administration, teaching-research, and research. Each respondent was asked to check which description applied best to his position. Initially, at least, it was felt that those in positions of administrative leadership would have a clearer grasp of norms that elsewhere, particularly in the hybrid function of teaching-research, might be regarded ambiguously. This idea seemed plausible because political scientists, in analyzing the macropolitical system,[40] had found that democratic norms are much more strongly held by individuals in positions of high status, influence, and leadership than by those in less prominent categories. Surprisingly, however, this attitude turns out to be incorrect, insofar as organized skepticism and emotional neutrality are concerned. In fact, conditions are not altered even if administrative positions are *not* considered the most powerful or influential ones within the autonomous system. As Appendix Figures C.19–C.20 show, both norms are either clearly rejected or ambiguously held by all "occupational" clusters. Those in administrative positions respond uncertainly to emotional neutrality and overwhelmingly indicate that the strictures of organized skepticism do not apply to their conception of scientific work. Scientists exclusively engaged in research have ambiguous attitudes toward both norms, while those who combine teaching and research reject emotional neutrality and respond ambiguously to organized skepticism.

The conclusion, then, to which one is driven is that the above hypothesis is false, that on the basis of the assembled data, patterns of ambiguity are not a function of "occupational" groupings.

Ambiguity Patterns (Type I). The autonomous system is also confronted by ambiguous attitudes (type I) toward universalism — a norm that justifies scientific inquiry as an activity independent of social and cultural bias. The emergence of this form of ambiguity is not quite so difficult to account for as the former type, since it represents a relatively clear division of opinion within the autonomous community. When referents are used that describe science as maintaining common objective standards,

[40] McClosky and Schaar, "Psychological Dimensions"; see footnote 31, especially the studies by Prothro and Grigg and McClosky.

or working from a standardized nomenclature transcending national boundaries, attitude responses overwhelmingly affirm its universal posture (see Table 3.8). But when scientists are asked whether the acceptance or rejection of scientific evidence may not in part depend upon the social position of the one who submits it (i.e., his institutional affiliation, his degree of recognition, his having studied under prominent men), the answer given is "yes" — which creates doubts about the two previous responses.

This condition is supported by the previous argument that scientists, like the electorate in general, can endorse a norm of generalized significance but withdraw their support if it is reduced to more concrete circumstances. After stratifying the responses to each referent (see Appendix Figures C.1–C.12) by institution, age, discipline, and "occupation," one finds no new evidence to alter this interpretation.

However, three items of information emerging from these figures should be mentioned. Question 22, which was constructed to probe the relation between social position and scientific evidence, created ambiguous attitudes in mathematics and in the group of scientists associated with the California Institute of Technology. Perhaps it is not puzzling why mathematicians gave an ambiguous response to this question. Modern mathematics represents a self-contained body of knowledge that is not empirically oriented. Empirical methods may from time to time be used for the discovery of new mathematical properties, but they cannot be recognized as elements of a *proof*. Question 22 does not concern the problem of proof, but only that of empirical evidence and whether it is to some extent socially conditioned. Mathematicians answering the question may therefore have been uncertain about how its content applied to their discipline. Even though the reaction of mathematicians to Question 22 can perhaps be explained, the response from the California Institute of Technology is completely baffling. Since mathematicians do not seem proportionately large in that sample, its unexpected response remains unjustified.

A third item of information must also go unexplained. Question 29, meant to probe attitudes toward a standardized, transnational nomenclature in science, was ambiguously answered by the University of Idaho (see Appendix Figure C.2). The response data give no clues why this is so. Since the sample is small, some influence could have been exerted by the cultural isolation of the university itself, but this inference does not seem justifiable — even at an intuitive level. Undoubtedly local factors bear upon this response, but to uncover them, one would have to explore the university much more thoroughly than is possible in a survey questionnaire.

CONCLUSION

The themes developed in this chapter, although operationally complex, are inherently simple ones. First, professionalized science is structurally supported by university departments, each victimized by the "entropy" of expanding scientific specialization. Even though the autonomous system is severely strained by these conditions, university scientists clearly prefer it to other "organizational" alternatives. Moreover, the autonomous system is given ideological support by the interest of scientists in distinguishing between pure and applied research. Pure research is thought to generate few, if any, demands for outside control. Its defense can therefore be seen as an attempt to preserve the epistemic objectives, as well as the clarity and focus of autonomous inquiry.

Second, the social norms of the autonomous system contribute to the perceptive capacity of scientific inquiry by regulating interpersonal goals and conflicts — in short, by allowing the "politics of science" to serve as a sensor to the external world. Yet, all the norms associated with the autonomous system are not positively endorsed. Scientists regard the norms of *universalism, organized skepticism,* and *emotional neutrality* with differing degrees of ambiguity. Universalism is strongly supported when its meaning is associated with international communication and objective standards of reason. But it is clearly rejected as an operating principle of research. In fact, scientists quite candidly admit that the acceptance of scientific evidence is not unrelated to the social position of the one who submits it. Organized skepticism and emotional neutrality reveal ambiguous attitudes of a different order. Both generate collective responses that indicate *indecisive* feelings of support and rejection — a posture that may have anomic implications.

The ambiguous attitudes toward all three norms involve a complicated interplay between the psychological and sociological features of scientific inquiry. Although it is not clear which predominates, the evidence examined thus far shows that such sociological factors as institutional prestige, age, academic discipline, and type of work do not exercise a decisive influence. A much more convincing explanation may lie in the attempt by scientific disciplines to create a consensual framework of knowledge. Once this process becomes evident, ambiguous tendencies can perhaps be attributed to the tensions between individual will and collegial criticism. How consensual frames of reference develop and what they mean for the "politics of science" constitute the subject matter of Chapter 4.

4

The political process
of science

THE PURPOSE of professionalized science, as understood by the members of the autonomous system, is to inquire freely into nature [1] in order to create a systematic, intelligible expression (or description) of reality. This undertaking, which is not fully understood by scientists themselves, is complicated because nature yields an abundance of puzzling and "inconsistent" data that can be perceived in a variety of patterns and from many different frames of reference. Scientists do not clearly understand because they have not sufficiently probed the social system within which they work and by which their perceptions are conditioned. The result is that scientific purpose is frequently confused with (or mistaken for) scientific practice, and a myth of science emerges that grossly misrepresents the strengths, as well as the weaknesses, of scientific inquiry.

One can uncover a prominent feature of this myth by focusing

---

[1] In 1960 the AAAS Committee on Science in the Promotion of Human Welfare argued that the fundamental purpose of scientific research was "the free inquiry into nature." *Science*, Vol. 132, no. 69 (1960).

attention on the distinction that is sometimes made between the social sciences and the natural sciences. Well-known scientists argue that the natural sciences "present a picture of the world as it appears to an observer outside the system" while the social sciences "present a picture of the world from inside the system." [2] This contrast is drawn usually to show how difficult it is for the social sciences to achieve an objective, "detached" view of their subject matter. Thus, according to the myth, what the natural scientist thinks about the order of planetary orbits does not influence planetary behavior at all, but what the social scientist thinks about the social order may have a definite impact upon the course and movement of society itself.

This distinction and the whole issue that it raises is unfortunate because it states the problem wrongly. The point is not "can scientific thought actually influence the order of planetary orbits," but rather, "what pattern of planetary orbits is 'seen' when examined from the paradigm of Copernican astronomy that cannot be seen when observed from the older, Ptolemaic model." Thomas Kuhn gives the answer:

> In the Ptolemaic system the planets were arranged in earth-centered orbits so that the average distance between a planet and the earth increased with the time required for the planet to traverse the elliptic. . . . the order of their orbits had therefore always been a source of debate. In the Copernican system there is no place for similar debate; no two planets have the same orbital period. The moon is no longer involved in the problem, for it travels about the earth rather than about the central sun. The superior planets, Mars, Jupiter, and Saturn, preserve their old order about the new center, because their orbital periods are the same as the average lengths of time they need to circle the elliptic. The earth's orbit lies inside of Mars's, since the earth's orbital period, 1 year, is less than Mars's 687 days. It only remains to place Mercury and Venus in the system, and their order is, for the first time, uniquely determined.[3]

[2] Anatol Rapoport draws this distinction in his "The Scientific Relevance of C. Wright Mills" in I. L. Horowitz, ed., *The New Sociology* (New York: Oxford University Press, 1965), p. 104.

[3] Thomas Kuhn, *The Copernican Revolution* (New York: Modern Library Paperbacks, Random House, 1957), pp. 173–174.

Research paradigms such as the Copernican system are pattern statements, to use Hanson's formulation,[4] that make observational details intelligible. In themselves they do not change the observable constituents of the world, but they do determine how these objects will be interpreted. Precisely this function influences our perceptions of reality and creates the cognitive modes through which we extend our knowledge of the physical universe.

Not all research models are as grand as Copernican astronomy — many in fact deal with phenomena that can be detected only with the most sophisticated instruments — but their functions are essentially the same: structuring data to make reality more intelligible. Once this principle is grasped, concern shifts to how pattern statements or models are generated and developed within scientific professions. Scientists must decide which models, in their collective judgment, offer the most reliable and consistent explanations of reality. Here, too, the conventional distinction between the natural and social sciences breaks down completely.

To explore the problem further, one must view scientific professions as miniature social orders, governed by procedures which turn research activities into systems of perceptual control. True, all professions are not alike — some are more fully developed and consequently less inclined to conflict than others — but it is also true that built-in tensions and problems characterize them all. Analytically these difficulties derive from two sources. The first is a product of the multiplicity of nature itself; conflicting interpretations of phenomena are possible because scientific models can rarely, if ever, account completely for observational data accumulated in the course of normal investigation.[5] The

[4] Norwood Russell Hanson, *Patterns of Discovery* (Cambridge: University Press, 1965), p. 87.

[5] A Princeton physicist, responding to the survey questionnaire, developed this point with admirable clarity: "The average layman, and indeed too many scientists, fail to appreciate that a theory is not a fact. Theories often are based on rather limited data, or data chosen to fit a theory, or based on little more substantial than philosophy. Examples of such theories are Hoyle's steady state theory of the universe, Einstein's theory of general relativity, and perhaps the various evolutionary hypotheses. Evolution, for instance, has not been shown to be able to explain all the available data,

second comes from pressures to conform to consensually designated "research problems," while at the same time satisfying one's own creative, and possibly deviant, curiosity.

The heat and controversy emerging within scientific professions, their duration, their "casualties," and their eventual resolution suggest that the purposes of scientific inquiry are actually furthered by social processes that, to a large degree, limit and control the interpretative scope of scientific research. These social processes are not the only means, of course, by which the goals of the autonomous system are advanced, since the sophisticated hardware for measuring and exposing scientific phenomena are absolutely essential in providing access to data beyond the range of unaided sense perception. What is frequently, and unfortunately, overlooked is that alone these devices do not have the capacity to interpret the data they have "sensed." The only "machine" that can both capably and reliably perform this function belongs to the whole social system of science and its ability to develop "a consensus of rational opinion"[6] — one that can partially explain the multiplicity of nature and, at the same time, satisfy the internal demands within scientific professions for a systematic and intelligible account of the natural world. In the words of a Stanford geologist:

> The strength of science lies in its specific design for the development and extension of communal knowledge. No other human endeavor is so specifically organised exclusively for the mutual instruction of those who participate in it. This emphasis on communal acceptance by a consensus of individuals is the socially significant aspect of the scientific method. More people should be made aware of the nature of this basic strut of our structure.[7]

Thus, the "politics of science" can be defined as a collective method for selecting and perpetuating ("enforcing") consensual

---

nor has enough of a *detailed* theory been worked out to even plausibly show the steps whereby, for instance, a one-celled organism could have arisen."

[6] John M. Ziman, *Public Knowledge* (Cambridge: University Press, 1968), p. 9.

[7] From the survey questionnaire.

patterns of perception and ultimately ordering them into a convincing, intelligible picture (model) of some aspect of the natural world. Although this process does not permit "freedom" in the same sense that a democratic citizen would understand it, membership in the autonomous system is completely voluntary, and those who wish to enter are expected to sacrifice their individual tempers to the consensual ideal.

The uncertainty accompanying this adjustment has previously been mentioned as a central problem in maintaining the "spatial" integrity of the autonomous system. What has not been discussed is how the consensus principle influences the content of scientific work. Specifically, this chapter covers (1) the nature of consensual research and its attendant configurations of power, (2) the emergence and resolution of scientific disputes, and (3) the problems that the impact of this research creates for legitimizing the activities of science to the larger community.

THE CONSENSUAL NATURE OF SCIENTIFIC RESEARCH

The distinctive feature of scientific research is its quest for a consensual interpretation of the natural world — a style of inquiry, to borrow Boring's characterization, in which empirical truth is affirmed through agreement.[8] The romantic vision of an isolated scientist who struggles to penetrate the secrets of nature is largely overdrawn and, if taken seriously, detrimental to scientific values. Science is not fundamentally an entrepreneurial enterprise; it is rather a corporate activity maintained by social processes specifically directed toward the realization of collective agreement. Ziman expounds the matter this way:

> The cliché of scientific prose betrays itself "Hence *we* arrive at the conclusion that. . . ." The audience to which scientific publications are addressed is not passive; by its cheering or booing, its bouquets or brickbats, it actively controls the substance of the communications that it receives.

[8] Edwin G. Boring, "The Validation of Scientific Belief," *Proceedings of the American Philosophical Society* 96, no. 5 (1952): 535.

But he is even more insistent, for he goes on to argue that

> science is not merely *published* knowledge or information. Any-
> one may make an observation, or conceive a hypothesis, and, if
> he has the financial means, get it printed and distributed for
> other persons to read. Scientific knowledge is more than this. Its
> facts and theories must survive a period of critical study and
> testing by other competent and disinterested individuals, and
> must have been found so persuasive that they are almost uni-
> versally accepted. *The objective of Science is not just to ac-
> quire information nor to utter all noncontradictory notions; its
> goal is a consensus of rational opinion over the widest possible
> field.*[9]

The commitment of science to a consensual interpretation of
natural phenomena serves two functions: it is, first of all, a form
of perceptual economy; second, it is a guide to areas of research
that are considered likely to produce important empirical results.
Yet the variety and complexity of nature present conditions
under which an abundance of perceptions is possible. Since all
perceptions are neither equally penetrating nor valid, some measure must be devised that can direct scientific inquiry only to
those that have a high degree of interest and reliability. Precisely
this task is performed by the consensus principle: relevant perceptions are selectively aggregated, first to define the substantive
concerns of scientific practice, and second, to resolve specific
problems entailed by these definitions.

The substantive focus of scientific inquiry is thus determined
by the structure of research paradigms that, as Kuhn suggests,
"provide models from which spring particular coherent traditions
of scientific research." Each paradigm represents a consensual
agreement that only certain lines of research have utility in exploring the perceived events of the natural world. Each functions,
then, as an exercise in recreating reality in essentially manageable
terms — which means excluding as too costly for further study
those perceptions that cannot be compressed within the para-

---

[9] Ziman, *Public Knowledge*, p. 9. [emphasis mine]

digm.[10] Moreover, the whole meaning of normal scientific research and training depends upon the successful operation of the consensus rule. Without it, scientific resources could not be efficiently allocated, and the quality of scientific perception might become less reliable, since there would be perhaps more room for serious disagreements over the nature and direction of scientific research. Kuhn forcefully grasps this point when he observes:

> The success of a paradigm . . . is at the start largely a promise of success discoverable in selected and still incomplete examples. Normal science consists in the actualization of that promise, an actualization achieved by extending the knowledge of those facts that the paradigm displays as particularly revealing, by increasing the extent of the match between those facts and the paradigm's predictions, and by further articulation of the paradigm itself.
> . . . By focusing attention upon a small range of relatively esoteric problems, the paradigm forces scientists to investigate some part of nature in a detail and depth that would otherwise be unimaginable. And normal science possesses a built-in mechanism that ensures the relaxation of the restrictions that bound research whenever the paradigm from which they derive ceases to function effectively. At that point scientists begin to behave differently, and the nature of their research problems changes. In the interim, however, during the period when the paradigm is successful, the profession will have solved problems that its members could scarcely have imagined and would never have undertaken without commitment to the paradigm. And at least part of that achievement always proves to be permanent.[11]

Profligate or uneconomic distribution of scientific effort might mean loss of both detail and penetration in scientific research.

[10] See, for example, Kuhn's statement of the point in Thomas Kuhn, *The Structure of Scientific Revolutions* (Chicago: University of Chicago Press, 1962), p. 5. "Normal science, the activity in which most scientists inevitably spend almost all of their time, is predicated on the assumption that the scientific community knows what the world is like. Much of the success of the enterprise derives from the community's willingness to defend that assumption, if necessary at considerable cost. Normal science, for example, often suppresses fundamental novelties because they are necessarily subversive of its basic commitments."

[11] *Ibid.*, pp. 23–25.

Therefore, the consensus rule is a hedge against cognitive extravagance, for it controls the acceptable limits of scientific thought.

Consensus and Scientific Investment. As a corollary to providing focus and depth for research behavior, the consensus principle also minimizes the risks of scientific investment, both for the individual scientist and for those who wish to support him. Perhaps the greatest personal risk that a scientist runs is selecting research problems. This choice is particularly hazardous for a young scientist immediately following the completion of his doctorate, but before receiving a tenured appointment. To reduce the prospects of failure, a scientist in this category must cast about for problems that are sufficiently "consensible" to insure respect and that utilize techniques whose results are rather clearly defined. An approach that does not fit well-established models of research or an experiment that involves the manipulation of rather novel techniques may prove professionally disastrous. A distinguished physicist summarized this situation as follows:

> I believe that it is risky for a young scientist to go off in directions which are so novel that results are not reasonably well assured. The risk here is particularly great, probably, between the stage of getting a Ph.D. degree and then obtaining a tenure position in a university or industry. After all, the chances of obtaining a permanent position are crucially dependent on peer evaluation based on visible research performance during this short period.[12]

It is not the young scientist alone who is drawn to invest in hypotheses with the "capital" provided by consensual paradigms. Older scientists — men of established reputations — often find it convenient and satisfying to temporize their research by deferring to the experimental standards of the prevailing consensus. They may do so for a number of reasons. First, they are likely to have a rather large investment of time and memory in a particular

---

[12] The scientist interviewed is a Professor of Physics, at the University of California (Berkeley). For observations that parallel these, see Fred Reif and Anselm Strauss, "The Impact of Rapid Discovery upon the Scientist's Career," *Social Problems* 12 (Winter 1965): 301.

research tradition. Their level of experimental achievement, the way in which they conceive the basic problems of science, and their preoccupation with specific research techniques all derive from intensive training within a particular paradigm. Second, the established scientists maintain a number of commitments to graduate students, postdoctoral fellows, and technicians who are dependent upon their ability to generate researchable problems and to provide continuing financial support. As one might expect, the most available problems are usually those that previous work has suggested or that can be seen as "spinoffs" from previous accomplishments. Third, to sustain their commitments to research, established scientists must secure grants or contracts, and these are likely to be awarded to those who are continuing well-established lines of research [13] – again emphasizing the importance of previous research as a guideline for future investment.

Consensual research commitments not only provide the foundation for normal scientific work, but they also highly influence the cost-benefit evaluation that granting institutions make to determine where their money is likely to receive its greatest return. As Harvey Brooks has argued: "A rough rule of thumb seems to be that on the average it costs about twice as much in the first year to start a research project in little science in a new location than it does to support a project where there is already work going on in the same or a closely related field." [14] Hence, in large measure, institutional grants are committed to levels of previous investment, and these in turn reflect the consensual attitude of the scientific community as to what areas are ready for research exploitation.

Michael Polanyi has fully endorsed this aspect of science, for it offers, in his view, the greatest prospect for advancing science along its many frontiers.[15] He insists that three factors condition the consensual evaluation of scientific research and clearly delineate the investment opportunities available for institutional support. These factors are the exactitude of a field, "its systematic

[13] *Ibid.*, p. 306.

[14] Harvey Brooks, *The Government of Science* (Cambridge, Mass.: The M.I.T. Press, 1968), p. 202.

[15] Michael Polanyi, "The Growth of Science in Society," *Minerva* 5 (Summer 1967): 543.

importance, and the intrinsic interest of its subject matter." Yet he continues:

> The proportion in which these factors enter into scientific value varies greatly over the different domains of science: deficiency in one factor may be balanced by greater excellence in another. The highest degree of exactitude and widest range of systematisation are found in mathematical physics, and this compensates for the lesser intrinsic interest of its inanimate subject. At the other end of the sciences, we have domains like zoology and botany which lack exactitude and have no systematic structure comparable in range . . . to that of physics, but which make up for this deficiency by the far greater intrinsic interest of living things compared with inanimate matter.[16]

Scientific value therefore depends upon the consensual balance that is struck among the factors of exactitude, system, and interest. Unless this point is firmly grasped, Polanyi maintains, the whole structure of scientific inquiry and the quality of scientific investment will be misunderstood. What is at issue is the essential process through which the scientific community seeks to achieve the "highest total increment" of knowledge by maximizing its marginal yield.

> The assessment of scientific value is . . . the principal standard by which the institutional structure of the scientific community is determined. Funds and appointments serving scientific research must be distributed in a way that promises the highest total increment to science. . . . This does not mean that one has to compare the scientific value of one *entire branch of science* with another. It requires only that we be able to compare the value of *scientific increments* achieved in the various branches of science at similar costs of effort and money. The marginal principle of economics offers the conceptual model for this: we must try to keep equal the marginal yield, in terms of scientific value, all along the advancing borders of the sciences.[17]

Implicit in the marginality argument is a plea for calculated commitment. Polanyi urges that it is both reasonable and useful to support scientific effort, even if one does not understand it,

[16] *Ibid.*, pp. 542–543.
[17] *Ibid.*, p. 543.

because it represents the critical consensus of those actively involved with advancing scientific knowledge. Yet the commitment required is not to some absolute ideal, but to a consensus rule that, expressed across the full spectrum of scientific specialization, makes possible an economy of energy by differentially adjusting investment opportunities.

> Thus an *indirect consensus* is formed between scientists so far apart that they could not understand more than a small part of each other's subjects. It is enough that the standards of plausibility and worthwhileness be equal around every single point for this will keep them equal over all the sciences. Scientists from the most distant branches of science will rely then on each other's results and will blindly support each other against any layman seriously challenging a scientist's professional authority.
>
> This is the way the scientific community is organized. These are the grounds on which science rests.[18]

Scientific commitment to the consensus rule not only functions as a guide to economy and efficiency in research but also serves as a symbol of legitimacy. It underscores the confidence that scientists may have in existing paradigms and justifies the exploration of specific hypotheses that are suggested by the variables these paradigms create. Thus, at all times, the legitimizing effect of the consensus principle operates at two levels of scientific activity — first in the support of research paradigms that continue a particular research tradition and, second, in the selection and confirmation of relevant hypotheses that articulate a paradigm's predictive magnitude.[19]

Because science is not a static enterprise, however, crises of legitimacy can and do occur. As might be expected, their effect is rather significant for established scientific disciplines, which are often committed to a single research paradigm and to the puzzle-solving routines carried out in its behalf. Less developed fields are not so deeply disturbed because they are not organized behind one research tradition, but several. A legitimacy crisis in one area does not mean that the entire discipline will be thrown

---

[18] *Ibid.*, p. 544.

[19] See Thomas Kuhn's comments about normal research in *The Structure of Scientific Revolutions*, p. 24.

into a state of unusual agitation and unrest. As often as not, the crisis marks the beginning of a further stage of maturation where achieving greater unity requires the abandonment of conflicting or unrelated paradigms. A crisis here may only accentuate a tendency to unify the discipline around a paradigm that can accommodate, or perhaps even redefine, fundamental aspects of those previously regarded as separate.

Legitimacy crises most frequently occur at the level of hypothesis selection and confirmation. Specific hypotheses may prove upon careful inspection to be useless as aids to the puzzle-solving tasks of normal science and hence lose their meaning and relevance. This loss may derive from an inability to secure convincing or unequivocal evidence in their favor, or it may result from a realization that, even if confirmed, the findings would not bear upon the very problems against which they are deployed. Such crises, however, mean only that better, more persuasive hypotheses are needed in order to satisfy the higher expectations of relevance.

Under normal circumstances, the conflicts accompanying this search are apt to be noncumulative and dispersed, which gives ample time for locating new hypotheses that can bridge the gap between expectation and practice. But there are periods of exploration that are unable to resolve the anomalies of normal research. If perplexing anomalies persist, the legitimacy of a whole paradigm may be called into question. As Kuhn has made plain:

> When . . . an anomaly comes to seem more than just another puzzle of normal science, the transition to crisis and to extraordinary science has begun. The anomaly itself now comes to be more generally recognized as such by the profession. More and more attention is devoted to it by more and more of the field's most eminent men. If it still continues to resist, as it usually does not, many of them may come to view its resolution as *the* subject matter of their discipline. For them the field will no longer look quite the same as it had earlier. Part of its different appearance results simply from the new fixation point of scientific scrutiny. An even more important source of change is the divergent nature of the numerous partial solutions that concerted attention to the problem has made available. . . . Through this proliferation of divergent articulations (more and more frequently they will come to be described as *ad hoc* adjustments),

the rules of normal science become increasingly blurred. Though there still is a paradigm, few practitioners prove to be entirely agreed about what it is.[20]

Since the consensus rule is more pronounced and effective in disciplines united behind a single paradigm, legitimacy crises that question it are matters for serious concern. And for good reason. Consensually endorsed paradigms constitute the only orthodoxy recognized by the autonomous community of science. In defining the major parameters of scientific study, these paradigms are largely responsible for creating the acceptable belief patterns through which scientists respond to the external world. In more than a superficial way paradigm crises resemble constitutional crises in which established institutional arrangements are confronted by forces that represent a new model of society, a new way of defining the goals and purposes of collective life.

Scientific Research and Scientific Orthodoxy. Although scientific orthodoxy can be seen as a functional consequence of the consensus principle, perhaps its presence is necessary in scientific research, for it reduces the possibilities of chaos and regulates the level of permissible dissent. As Bernard Cohen has cogently argued:

> Had scientists no orthodoxy, and if they welcomed with avidity every possible idea that anyone might have, the scientific enterprise would be characterized by chaos rather than positive achievement and progress.
>
> The creative life is all too short to be wasted in considering every imaginable novelty merely because it is novel. Scientists have, therefore, wisely restricted themselves to paths that have seemed to promise fruitfulness. For example, even before there was any proof by mathematicians that it was impossible to square the circle, the French Academy of Sciences decided that it would no longer examine . . . proofs that were submitted to it of the squaring of the circle. They didn't believe that the circle could be squared, although no proof of the impossibility of this construction was at hand; but economy insisted that the time of the mathematicians who belonged to the Academy could be better

20 *Ibid.*, pp. 82–83.

spent than in examining every pretended solution of this problem. The same procedure was wisely adopted with regard to proposals for perpetual motion machines — long before the establishment of principles indicating that the construction of such machines would be inconsistent with physical science — and also attempts to duplicate the cube or trisect the angle.[21]

The usefulness and propriety of scientific orthodoxy is further reinforced by Michael Polanyi, who fears that the popular image of science (the vision of science as an unbiased pursuit of knowledge) obscures the professional necessity for restricting dissent. As a young scientist, Polanyi proposed a rather innovative theory about the adsorption of gases on solid surfaces.[22] Because his theory was at variance with the prevailing consensus on intermolecular forces, it was disregarded. Recently, however, scientific opinion has been shifting more and more in Polanyi's direction, giving his theory the aspect of respectability. In responding to this turn of events — after waiting 49 years — Polanyi speaks directly to the whole issue of opposition and orthodoxy in scientific inquiry:

> I repeat here that I am not arguing against the present balance between the powers of orthodoxy and the rights of dissent in science. I merely insist on acknowledgement of the fact that the scientific method is, and must be, disciplined by an orthodoxy which can permit only a limited degree of dissent, and that such dissent is fraught with grave risks to the dissenter. I demand a clear recognition of this situation for the sake of our intellectual honesty as scientists, and I charge that this situation is not recognized today but is, on the contrary, obscured by current declarations about science. Take this by Bertrand Russell:
>
>> The triumphs of science are due to the substitution of observation and inference for authority. Every attempt to revive authority in intellectual matters is a retrograde step. . . .

[21] I. Bernard Cohen, "Orthodoxy and Scientific Progress," *Proceedings of the American Philosophical Society* 96 (October 1952): 509–510.

[22] Michael Polanyi, "The Potential Theory of Adsorption: Authority in Science Has Its Uses and Dangers," *Science* 141, no. 3585 (September 1963): 1010–1013.

Such statements obscure the fact that the authority of current scientific opinion is indispensable to the discipline of scientific institutions; that its functions are invaluable, even though its dangers are an unceasing menace to scientific progress.[23]

The sensitivity that scientists have toward orthodoxy in research is reflected by the high premium placed upon communication. Orthodoxy is simply an attitude of mind established by prevailing scientific opinion, on what is considered theoretically sound and deserving of support. But since scientific specialization has exposed a wide variety of problems, it is necessary to constantly monitor the direction of opinion shifts in response to new information. This makes communication all-important in scientific research and sensitizes scientists to the presence of consensual control. Scientists, in fact, are quite candid about this state of affairs. As our survey questionnaire shows (see Table 4.1), they overwhelmingly believe that scientific progress cannot be explained as the creation of new ideas or the development of new methods and experiments. To be of any use, scientific innovations must be effectively communicated to others.

Politics, Consensus, and Perception. Although the consensus principle stands as the ultimate symbol of scientific orthodoxy, it does not explain the dynamics by which differing scientific opinions are transformed into consensual commitments. The major premise of this study is that the "transformation factor" is supplied by politics — a process that enables consensual results to emerge as temporary stabilities achieved within situations of conceptual diversity and disagreement. Viewed from this perspective, the politics of science is an essential tool of scientific perception, for it regulates conflicts, defines levels of acceptable research performance, and allocates research priorities.

To assert that politics is a requisite function of scientific perception is to maintain that techniques of influence and persuasion are a vital part of the way in which scientists are likely to interpret the world. Many scientists, to be sure, are repulsed by this notion and retreat behind the barriers of professional expertise

[23] *Ibid.*, p. 1013.

Table 4.1 Dependency of Scientific Progress upon Communication

Question	Num- ber	Strongly Agree	Agree	Can't Say	Dis- agree	Strongly Disagree	Total[b]
1[a]	849	57%	40%	1%	1%	0%	99%

[a] Question 1: "For science to be advanced it is not enough that fruitful ideas be originated, or new experiments developed, or new methods instituted; the innovations must be effectively *communicated* to others."

[b] Percentages are rounded to nearest whole number, so the total does not equal 100%.

to create an antiseptic impression of science. Others respond by denying completely that science is involved with internal politics, implying that a mixture of the two is not only unwise, but unsound and unscientific. Astronomer Cecilia Payne-Gaposchkin clearly reveals these purist notions when she writes:

> Scientists may congratulate themselves that they are not, as such, required to swear to anything. Nonetheless, every scientific man, every man who devotes his life sincerely to the advancement of knowledge, commits himself to certain loyalties. His loyalties are to principles, not to dogmas; to respect for evidence — all the evidence, not merely such as fulfills his expectations, and respect for those formulations that embody the evidence. We who are engaged in research are not concerned in preserving the existing framework of theories. We spend our lives searching for the wherewithal to modify and supplant them. The discovery of discordant facts is cause for rejoicing, not consternation.[24]

In responding to the questionnaire, an astronomer at the University of Arizona furnished additional insight into the antiseptic characterization of science. In his judgment,

> the only motivation required for a research scientist is an abiding curiosity about his environment — particularly that portion of it he has chosen to be *most* active in. All else follows: objectivity, dispassionate accretion of physical data about the environment as modified by his experiments, application of the results from the

[24] Quoted in Alfred de Grazia, *et al.*, eds., *The Velikovsky Affair* (New York: University Books, 1966), p. 176.

data to new boundary conditions or constraints, re-observation, interpretation, etc., etc., . . . *ad infinitum.*

From the same survey, a Berkeley physicist and a Harvard biochemist lend further support to this version of scientific inquiry – the former suggests that to be a scientist is "to be part of an unselfish, but very rewarding effort to increase human knowledge and understanding; an effort which offers the only real hope for bettering the average human condition"; and the latter insists:

> Scientists are very diverse . . . Some – the best, I think – do their work because they are seeking a deeper understanding of the nature of the universe, of life, and of man. They go through periods of anguish and of exaltations; much of the time they must concentrate on careful study of details, but this is illuminated by seeing one's particular problem in a much wider context, and as part of a far-reaching attempt to gain a deeper understanding of nature.

Not all scientists, of course, hold these attitudes, but their persistence and seeming naïveté has led at least one critic to create a rather stunning caricature of the entire scientific enterprise.

> Science is a – what? a method, a faith, a body of facts, a structure of theories, an institution, a way of life, a finite number of duly qualified individuals, an infinity of relevance and possibility. For a large number of scientists, science is indescribable, but indisputably a *thing:* it is knowable, palpable, reliable, usable. They live with it and by it; it is simply and unequivocally *there.*
> . . . The only thing wrong with scientists is that they don't know where their own institution came from, what forces shaped and are still shaping it, and they have wedded themselves to an antihistorical way of thinking which threatens to deter them from ever finding out.[25]

This description is intentionally hyperbolic and reflects, surely more than anything else, a deep-seated frustration that scientists have not concerned themselves with the institutional dynamics

[25] Eric Larrabee, "Science and the Common Reader," *Commentary,* June 1966, p. 43; second paragraph, p. 48.

through which their perceptual biases are mobilized and sustained. There seems to be, in fact, a lingering suspicion that if science is shown to have political features it must submit to the same tests of responsibility as the larger political world. And if it somehow fails to prove itself by these standards, its autonomous position may be threatened, its work interrupted, and its power of consensual judgment reduced to formal procedures for insuring fair play.

Scientific Disciplines and Power Configurations. Yet all scientific disciplines are marked by configurations of power — by patterns of "authoritative" decision-making — which differ from discipline to discipline, and are structurally supported by the professionalized features of science itself. It is even possible, for example, to develop a typology of "regimes" that may typify broad contours of political interaction within scientific disciplines at various stages of development. One of the simplest and most attractive methods for creating such political distinctions lies in stratifying the scientific community along two dimensions: first, by locating the number of decision-makers responsible for passing judgment on scientific performance and, second, by determining the degree of theoretical consensus within the disciplines concerned. As Table 4.2 demonstrates, a minimum of four types of "regimes" can be derived from this stratification: communal polity, oligarchy, competitive plurality, and democracy. Although each "regime" represents an ideal type, it is useful in focusing upon aspects of scientific practice that may have important political functions. Analytically, of course, one regime is no more exemplary than another, but, as we shall see, a large number of scientists are not convinced of this and insist upon perpetuating a regime image of scientific behavior that does not conform to the actual conditions of research.

Insofar as the number of decision-makers is concerned, the communal polity posits the active participation of literally all who are interested in pursuing a particular scientific subject. The remaining regimes can be characterized by a rough calculation of the percentage of those permitted to engage in decision-making functions. A democratic regime would have to acknowl-

Table 4.2   TYPES OF POWER CONFIGURATIONS OR "REGIMES" WITHIN SCIENTIFIC DISCIPLINES

Degree of Theoretical Consensus	Number of Decision-Makers	
	Many	Few
High	Communal Polity	Oligarchy
Low	Democracy	Competitive Plurality

edge a participation factor of at least 51 per cent, while an oligarchic one might be expected to fluctuate as much as 20 per cent, depending upon how rigidly one wished to define crucial decisions. On the other hand, a competitive plurality might operate within a 25–40 per cent range of participation and still qualify as a distinct political regime.

Participation is only one dimension of the typology. If each regime is to represent a conjunction of two levels of stratification, it is necessary to establish degrees of consensus among them. In this connection, the communal polity assumes a complete unanimity of outlook and purpose — one deriving from a total commitment to a single paradigm. (It is difficult to imagine a regime of this type in the world of research, for as Kuhn has indicated: "the puzzles that constitute normal science exist only because no paradigm that provides a basis for scientific research ever completely resolves all its problems. The very few that have ever seemed to do so [e.g., geometric optics] have shortly ceased to yield research problems at all. . . .") [26] At the other extreme, a scientific democracy does not exhibit a strong attraction to any research model, but asserts the desirability of each individual's pursuing his own interests and gathering as many "facts" as possible. (This regime would find its closest approximations in very young disciplines — such as geology in the early nineteenth century and, to some extent, parapsychology in the twentieth.) In contrast, oligarchic regimes would be typified by close, but not total, adherence to a single research paradigm — one responsible for

---

[26] Kuhn, *The Structure of Scientific Revolutions*, p. 79.

keeping the intellectual momentum of a discipline highly focused and productive. (Most of the prestigious fields of study — for example, physics, astronomy, and chemistry — would be represented by this configuration of cohesion and interest.) The competitive plurality differs from the oligarchic structure in that there are several paradigms pursued within its compass, but its impetus is decidedly toward the unification of related research rather than in the more dispersed direction of a democratic regime. (The disciplines approaching this characterization today are biology and geology.)

The identification of scientific regimes is useful for an understanding of the politics of science, since each one establishes expectations governing the limits of what may be done to reconcile conflicts and settle controversies. Regimes provide the formal boundaries within which the perceptive claims of individuals and groups are legitimized, although they do not always determine how these claims are adjusted to each other.

Given the nature of the scientific community, only two types of adjustment patterns seem relevant. Both have been carefully and critically discussed by Charles Lindblom who characterizes them as *adaptive* and *manipulative* modes of response.[27] The adaptive response is one "in which a decision maker simply adapts to decisions around him, that is, makes those decisions that he can make without first enlisting, as in negotiation, a response from another decision maker"; while the manipulated response is exemplified by a decision-maker who tries to *enlist* a desired response from another decision-maker.[28] Once these two patterns of adjustment are applied to the collective behavior of scientists, one can distinguish two styles of action by which scientific perceptions are evaluated and controlled. One may be called the Criticism-Controversy-Adaptive Resolution model and the other a mode of response embodying Conflict-Competition and Manipulated Resolution. The scientific community prides itself on operating under the Criticism model while, in fact, it almost

[27] See Charles Lindblom's comments on patterns of coordination in his *Intelligence of Democracy* (New York: The Free Press, 1965), p. 33.
[28] *Ibid.*, p. 33.

always operates under the Conflict model. Precisely because conflict exists, one can speak meaningfully of the internal politics of science — or at least of political patterns in scientific work that move beyond the persuasiveness and power of mere rhetoric. Although perhaps more covertly utilized when compared to the behavior of the macropolitical world, the scientific community consistently makes use of rewards and sanctions to regulate the flow of acceptable information and, hence, the supply of legitimate perceptions.

To develop this argument further, it may be useful to follow the "official" statements of what "regime conditions" scientists feel are appropriate to their work, and how they explain the existence and resolution of perceptual disagreements. Most scientists insist, at least publicly, upon a variation of the communal polity, emphasizing a high degree of consensus and wide participation. As explained by prominent members of the profession, the scientific community constitutes a regime in which science is harmoniously advanced through mutual criticism, individual initiative, and respect for differing points of view. J. Robert Oppenheimer has sympathetically described this condition in the following terms:

> In any science there is harmony between practitioners. A man may work as an individual, learning of what his colleagues do through reading or conversation; he may be working as a member of a group on problems whose technical equipment is too massive for individual effort. But whether he is part of a team or solitary in his own study, he, as a professional, is a member of a community. His colleagues in his own branch of science will be grateful to him for the inventive or creative thoughts he has, will welcome his criticism. His world and work will be objectively communicable; and he will be quite sure that if there is error in it, that error will not long be undetected. In his own line of work he lives in a community where common understanding combines with common purpose and interest to bind men together both in freedom and in cooperation.[29]

[29] J. Robert Oppenheimer, *The Open Mind* (New York: Simon and Schuster, 1955), pp. 137–138.

Other characterizations of scientific research convey roughly the same impression. I. I. Rabi, speaking to the centennial celebration of the National Academy of Sciences, gave this interpretation:

> Scientists traditionally are free, untrammeled, and individualistic. Each sets his own goals following his interests. Such coordination as there is comes out of the nature of the subject matter and out of the tradition of the discipline; attempts to interfere, direct, or guide this freedom . . . result in inefficiency and frustration of the creative urge.
>   . . . Therein lies one of the greatest appeals of science . . . to be a member of a community which is free but not anarchical. . . . Members of this community possess an inner solidity which comes from a sense of achievement and an inner conviction that the advance of science is important and worthy of their greatest effort.[30]

John Ziman has recently warned that the scientific community must always remain open and critical:

> The community of those who are competent to contribute to, or criticize, scientific knowledge must not be closed; it must be larger, and more open, than the group of those who entirely accept a current consensus or orthodoxy. It is an essential element in the health of Science, or of a science, or of the sciences, that self-confirming, mutually validating circles be unable to close. Yet it is also essential that technical scientific discussion be not smothered in a cloud of ignorant prejudices and cranky speculations.[31]

From Ziman's warning, however, faint traces of concern are evident that perhaps the scientific community does not live up to its vaunted image, that care must be taken to prevent the emergence of "self-confirming, mutually validating" circles of influence. In fact, when one begins to study the dynamics of scientific inquiry, he finds that this fear is not without foundation. Immediately the question is raised why these conditions

[30] I. I. Rabi, *et al., The Scientific Endeavor,* Centennial Celebration of the National Academy of Sciences (New York: Rockefeller Institute Press, 1963), p. 308.
[31] Ziman, *Public Knowledge,* p. 64.

should provoke alarm. The answer, of course, is that scientists seek to legitimize their activities under the "rules of the game" laid down by the communal polity. Once these "rules" are internalized, it is easy to maintain that the perceptual disagreements emerging within this regime result from a free play of intellectual forces which are ultimately resolved by an appeal to reason and the rational experiment. Individual scientists are therefore expected to adapt their perceptual frames of reference eventually to those endorsed by a "consensus of rational opinion" over the entire field of qualified participants.

Yet neither the communal polity nor the adaptive resolution of perceptual differences makes allowance for the strategies and tactics of political influence within scientific inquiry. The "official" posture of the scientific community simply does not encourage recognition of these activities, for to do so might require a new standard for assessing the legitimacy of scientific work. The actual world of science, however, counteracts this image and reveals patterns of movement in which institutional elites are constantly forced to make judgments about conflicting perceptions, all of which contain a certain validity. Although the "official" image leaves the impression that scientific judgment is made in the light of standards transcending politics, an empirical assessment of what scientists do may create a strikingly different picture.

Regime Conditions, Stages of Theoretical Development, and Elite Relationships. In order to understand the "regime conditions" under which scientists operate, one must grasp the structural dimensions of the scientific community. The autonomous system of science is composed of a multiplicity of disciplines and subspecialties, some of which lag far behind others in their stage of theoretical development. Disciplines like physics, astronomy, and chemistry have tightly integrated theories, while biology and geology are still trying to reach this end. The degree of theoretical unity in a discipline is important to an understanding of conflict in a science because its unity conditions the kinds of disputes regarded as legitimate. Within disciplines in which a high degree of theoretical consensus prevails, conflicts are much more limited and sharply defined than in disciplines in which divergent "schools of thought" define entrenched positions. Three scientists — an atomic physicist, a theoretical physicist, and a chemist — tried to clarify why severe conflict is absent within their fields of interest.

Atomic physics is a rather well-established field of investigation and the disputes which arose in the early days are largely forgotten. I do not know of any outstanding differences in atomic theory.

While there are different "schools of thought" in the field of elementary particle physics, they cannot be said to be in violent dispute with one another. They represent different approaches to the basic problems of the field and the general expectation is probably that they will eventually coalesce. Each borrows ideas from the other and tries to embody them in its own approach. It should also be noted that there are no striking phenomena that one school can explain while another cannot.

Physicists generally accept quantum mechanics as the starting point for all discussion, but there does exist a small group, led by David Bohm of Bristol, who are not satisfied with its probabilistic point of view. This, however, tends to be more of a philosophical dispute on the sidelines.

If I were to define my field very narrowly, i.e., "nuclear magnetic resonance spectroscopy," I should say that there are no major theoretical disputes at this time. If I were to define it much more broadly, i.e., "chemistry" or even "physical chemistry," there would be quite a large number of disputes, though few if any would perhaps be considered of fundamental importance. Each one involves a relatively small group of workers primarily interested in the appropriate subarea of research.

No doubt it has already occurred to you that these disputes occur much more frequently in a "young" science such as molecular biology than in an "old" one like inorganic chemistry. Perhaps chemistry as a whole is no longer young enough to be characterized by significantly divergent schools of thought.

By contrast, in biology there are many disputes — all perhaps of some importance — but at least one questions whether we can adequately explain life-phenomena by our present knowledge of physical and chemical laws.[32] Perhaps another example is the field of cosmochemistry whose relatively young state creates a high level of conflict. A scientist working in this area summed up the probable reasons for this condition:

> There are so many areas under dispute in my fields of interest that to enumerate them would require many pages. In general these might be summarized by noting that these center on various theories of the origin of the solar system both in general and with particular emphasis on the Earth-Moon-Meteorites-Sun group. In each of these areas there are again many disputes. These all arise because (a) the topics are of great interest and importance, (b) the fields are young ones, (c) the data are present in relatively large amounts, and (d) theories to explain these data often conflict.

Occurrences of this nature are by no means unexpected, for in disciplines without firm theoretical commitments, strong tendencies are present for perpetuating "metaphysical" disputes and fundamental controversies.

The separation of scientific fields into different stages of theoretical development enables one to describe the politics of science much more precisely, for "regime conditions" can be specified for disciplines that have not attained full maturity. Theoretical development alone is not sufficient to indicate the character of the regime under which different disciplines operate. The number of decision-makers who are prominent in evaluating the significance of scientific work must be considered as well. Within all disciplines there are expanding circles of influence that define the scope of relevant decisions. As a Berkeley physicist put it: "In scientific inquiry acceptance depends much upon who is doing the accepting; my answer assumes that we are talking about acceptance by one whose acceptance is relevant."

It may be hypothesized that at the core of each discipline is a group of scientists who, in Polanyi's terminology, are the "chief Influentials" — those men likely to influence the direction of

[32] See Michael Polanyi, "Life Transcending Physics and Chemistry," *Chemical and Engineering News* 45, no. 35 (August 21, 1967): 55–66.

fundamental research by controlling appointments, promotions, publications, and the distribution of special subsidies and awards. Beyond the Influentials lie the Scientific Statesmen, whom Hagstrom has characterized as

> men with established reputations in their own disciplines [who] may devote much of their time to specialists in other fields and to non-scientists. Their prestige is secure enough for them to appear as experts to non-specialists without jeopardizing their reputations among their colleagues. . . . Scientists of this type have made contributions to their own field in the past and now contribute outside of it, while having relatively fewer informal contacts within it.[33]

At a distance from the Statesmen are the Student-Oriented Leaders and Intradepartmentally-Oriented Scientists. Both groups are usually outside the scope of significant decision-making and relate to their respective disciplines through the constituencies toward which they are oriented.[34] Still further removed are the Marginal Scientists. This group spends most of its time in consultation with nonspecialists and derives the bulk of its prestige and importance from the consulting bodies it serves.[35] Although part of a decision-making process that involves the application of science to larger society, the Marginal Scientists do not make the vital decisions affecting the growth of scientific disciplines.

The recognition that circles of influence may exist in science is contrary to the communal image used by scientists to legitimize their activities. Yet what is ultimately revealing is the possibility that only one of these circles – the chief Influentials – seems to make crucial decisions. The matter does not end here, for the relations among the Influentials depend upon the relative maturity of the disciplines. As Figure 4.1 illustrates, disciplines with a high degree of theoretical unity are likely to be characterized by interlocking elites, while those whose theoretical unity has not yet emerged, or is present only in intermediate form, are

---

[33] Warren O. Hagstrom, *The Scientific Community* (New York: Basic Books, 1965), p. 45.

[34] These descriptive types are discussed by Hagstrom, *ibid.*, pp. 45–46.

[35] *Ibid.*, p. 47.

perhaps controlled by competitive elites whose competences may overlap slightly or not at all. Thus the "regime conditions" under which science actually performs its tasks may depend upon the stage of disciplinary development and the proximity of the elite groups active in the field. Within the compass of the present study the oligarchic regime seems most descriptive for physics, astronomy, and chemistry, while the competitive plurality best defines the political dimensions of biology and geology.

A great number of scientists, however, do not believe that science has elitist qualities and continue to accept the communal ideal of scientific behavior. Additional evidence must therefore be presented in support of the elitist model before discussing the manipulative techniques used to insure consensual control. Two levels of evidence will be presented to demonstrate the plausibility of the elitist structure of science — the first originates from depth interviews with scientists and published accounts of scientific performance, and the second comes from statistical responses to the survey questionnaire.

One of the most revealing statements concerning the impact of elites upon scientific inquiry developed from an interview with a member of the National Academy and director of a prominent research institute. He noted:

> In my profession there is a canonizing of views. These are the views that are subscribed to by the most influential members of the profession. That is, those who are the editors of journals and the leading members of professional societies. These people are

Figure 4.1   ELITE CHARACTERISTICS IN DEVELOPED AND UNDERDEVELOPED DISCIPLINES

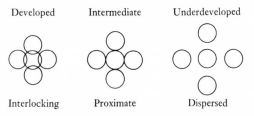

Each circle represents a subspecialty and each cluster of circles an entire discipline.

the defendants and judges of particular points of view. They are able to crush incompatible thoughts. But, of course, they do it under the guise that there is not enough evidence, or that the evidence is incomplete. You might say that there is a conspiracy of discrimination. Why? Because some people fear that their reputations are threatened or they fear for their economic position within universities. A new theory or innovative model creates certain insecurities.

In general I would say that the barrier to the advancement of science lies between the whole of a discipline and the in-group that controls the flow of discoveries. What happens is that there are flag-wavers in science as there are in the larger political system. In science the flag is not Old Glory, but "complete evidence." And many scientists turn themselves into apostles of complete evidence.

The organization of science is characterized by a certain insensitivity to new evidence — especially if it's revolutionary. But what is interesting to note is how the standards of evidence shift. If you take a traditional line, there is no opposition offered. If you take off on something new you expect to have trouble — sometimes, however, the trouble is without reasonable support. As I indicated earlier, the in-group of scientists are like judges. If the problem is routine, they may show great flexibility. If it is radical and different, they are likely to retreat to a position of complete conventionality.

Under such circumstances a young man would be utterly powerless to change the prevailing outlook. You have to be well-established or you will have no effect. I can have an impact because I am a member of the National Academy and have a direct outlet in the *Proceedings of the National Academy*. In addition I write books and lecture, as well as direct the institute here.

A professor of physics at Berkeley lends further credibility to the elitist structure of science by explaining the importance of its prestige systems and the necessity imposed upon scientists to operate under its constraints.

Another feature of interest concerns the people who set the standards against which the individual scientist appraises himself and whose opinion determines his general reputation in the field. It is mainly the well-established scientists in the major universities of the world who set these standards. Since the institution with which the individual scientist is affiliated tends to evaluate him chiefly on the basis of his reputation, it becomes of greater concern to the individual to seek the good opinion of people on the national or international scene than to strive for accomplishments which attract only local attention.

. . . Since the pure scientist's reputation, irrespective of the particular institution to which he belongs, is determined by the same reference group of prominent scientists, there exists a common prestige system which cuts across purely organizational lines.[36]

Whether in the allocation of prestige or in the control of papers that move through the principal channels of communication, the bias of the scientific community is against widespread participation in decisions directly affecting the evaluation of research. The restricted leadership of science is sometimes referred to as those who have the "best and wisest minds," but their function is unmistakable: to preserve high standards of inquiry by screening out suspect or divergent judgments. Ziman describes this situation from the perspective of one who is on the "inside":

Scientific knowledge is not created solely by the piecemeal mining of discrete facts by uniformly accurate and reliable individual scientific investigators. The processes of criticism and evaluation, of analysis and synthesis, are essential to the whole system. It is impossible for each one of us to be continually aware of all that is going on around us, so that we can immediately decide the significance of every new paper that is published. The job of making such judgments must therefore be delegated to the best and wisest among us, who speak, not with their own personal voices, but on behalf of the whole community of Science. Anarchy is as much a danger in that community as in any tribe or nation. It is impossible for the consensus – public knowledge – to be voiced at all, unless it is channelled through the minds of selected persons, and restated in their words for all to hear.[37]

---

[36] Fred Reif, "The Competitive World of the Pure Scientist," in Norman Kaplan, ed., *Science and Society* (Chicago: Rand McNally, 1965), pp. 138–139.

[37] Ziman, *Public Knowledge,* pp. 136–137.

Since Ziman's sympathy is enlisted on behalf of the active inner circle of scientists, it does not carry the analytical fervor of those who view the "scientific establishment" from the "outside." Such criticism is difficult to locate in published form because scientists are not only reluctant to air their "dirty linen" in public, but few wish to use the communication channels that are open to "debates" of this sort. Recently, however, *Playboy* magazine published an article called "Bucking the Scientific Establishment," [38] which elicited two "letters-to-the-editor" revealing how deeply some scientists feel about "establishment" politics.

> Ted Gordon's article in the April *Playboy* on *Bucking the Scientific Establishment* was well put, well chosen and well documented. As one who has published about 100 professional papers — in and out of establishment journals — I, too, have been buffeted. Gordon only omitted reference to the mental anguish that can result from conflicts with establishment ideology.

> As a former college teacher and consultant to several Government agencies, I can testify from years of personal experience to the stultifying and arrogant close-mindedness that affects much of today's supposedly open-minded scientific effort. . . . For all practical purposes, any evidence that does not conform with science as it is already *believed* is automatically rejected.[39]

These responses are deeply resentful, but Don K. Price has dispassionately argued the point:

> Most scientists are prepared to work most of the time within the framework of ideas developed by their acknowledged leaders. In that sense, within any discipline, science is ruled by oligarchs who hold influence as long as their concepts and systems are accepted as the most successful strategy.[40]

Although additional material is available from both historical accounts of scientific behavior and from the depth interviews, the existence of opinion in support of the elitist nature of science

[38] Ted Gordon, "Bucking the Scientific Establishment," *Playboy* 12, no. 4 (April 1968): 127 ff.

[39] *Playboy* 15, no. 7 (July 1968): 10.

[40] Don K. Price, *The Scientific Estate* (Cambridge, Mass.: Harvard University Press, 1965), p. 172.

should be apparent by now. The problem with evidence of this character is whether it reflects the way in which science is perceived by the rank-and-file membership of the scientific community. As already indicated, many scientists do not publicly admit to an elitist structure of their profession, and techniques must be developed for probing their attitudes more fully and accurately. Our survey questionnaire was designed specifically to meet this problem. By using a variety of questions from a number of different contexts, it sampled attitude dimensions across the panoply of scientific specialization. In all but one case — that dealing with the determination of acceptable evidence — questions meant to uncover elitist bias were answered unequivocally in the affirmative. Even in the matter of "acceptable evidence," responses were not clearly against the possible intrusion of position, "contacts," and prestige in determining what evidence to accept or reject. As Table 4.3 reveals, the ambiguity shown toward this vital area of scientific activity is striking. On the one hand, scientists deny that a small group — representing an even smaller cluster of universities and research laboratories — significantly determines what kinds of evidence are acceptable for hypothesis confirmation. On the other hand, they fully admit that the social position of scientists — defined in terms of their institutional affiliation, prestige, and those under whom they have

Table 4.3   ELITEST INFLUENCE UPON THE DETERMINATION OF
ACCEPTABLE EVIDENCE

Question	Num-ber	Strongly Agree	Agree	Can't Say	Dis-agree	Strongly Disagree	Total
8[a]	840	4%	27%	18%	42%	10%	101%
22[b]	840	5	28	7	53	7	100

[a] Question 8: "Within my discipline there is a small group (consistently representing a smaller cluster of universities and research labs) who highly influence what kinds of evidence are acceptable for the empirical confirmation of hypotheses."

[b] Question 22: "The acceptance or nonacceptance of scientific evidence does not in any way depend upon the social position of the one who submits it (that is, his institutional affiliation [university or lab], his degree of recognition, those under whom he has studied or worked)."

worked — has an impact upon the evaluation of evidence. What is also of interest is the insistence by many scientists who disagree with the idea of elitist determination of evidence that a small group does exist, but that its function is hypothesis *selection* rather than confirmation. Typical of these responses are the ones from an ecologist at Princeton and a biophysicist from Berkeley.

> In ecology there is no group that dictates the kinds of evidence needed to empirically confirm hypotheses. There are, however, only a very small number of men (fewer than 20) who have greatly affected the kinds of hypotheses that are proposed.

> The small group exists, but I do not think they determine what is *acceptable* empirical confirmation. Most everyone knows what is acceptable. The good guys are the ones who are smart enough to do the right experiments.[41]

As Table 4.4 illustrates, the areas within which positive endorsement is given to the elitist nature of inquiry are those that deal with (1) the control of key panel assignments at annual conventions and (2) the "Matthew Effect"[42] of science's prestige system. These oligarchical characteristics, however, do not represent the fortuitous combination of knowledge and skill, as the hagiographers of science suggest, but are largely the result of structural features within the scientific community itself. Elites do not happen; they are created, and the chief creators are men at prestigious institutions who control (1) recruitment and membership into the high echelons of scientific work, (2) the flow of communication, (3) appointments, (4) special subsidies, and (5) honorific awards. At least in this respect Michael Polanyi has correctly diagnosed the condition.

> The dominant powers [within science] . . . are exercised by referees advising on scientific appointments, on the allocation of

[41] Quoted from the survey questionnaire.

[42] The term "Matthew Effect" was coined by Robert K. Merton to stand for the misallocation of credit in scientific work. Inspiration for the concept derives from that part of the Gospel according to St. Matthew dealing with inequities in possessions. Robert K. Merton "The Matthew Effect in Science," *Science* 159, no. 3810 (January 5, 1969): 56–62.

Table 4.4   ELITEST INFLUENCE IN SCIENTIFIC ACTIVITY

Question	Num-ber	Strongly Agree	Agree	Can't Say	Dis-agree	Strongly Disagree	Total
4[a]	852	8%	37%	24%	27%	4%	100%
7[b]	850	21	60	9	9	1	100

[a] Question 4: "Within my discipline there has developed an inner group which, in large part, controls the key panel assignments at the annual association meetings."

[b] Question 7: "In papers co-authored by men of decidedly unequal reputations, or in findings submitted independently by a scientist of great repute and one not widely known, the man who is best known gets more credit than the other(s)."

special subsidies and on the award of distinctions. Advice on these points, which often involve major issues of the policy of science, is usually asked from and tendered by a small number of senior scientists who are universally recognized as the most eminent in a particular branch. They are the chief Influentials, the unofficial governors of the scientific community. By their advice they can either delay or accelerate the growth of a new line of research. They can provide special subsidies for new lines of research at any moment. By the award of prizes and of other distinctions, they can invest a promising pioneer almost overnight with a position of authority and independence. More slowly, but no less effectively, a new development can be stimulated by the policy pursued by the Influentials in advising on new appointments. Within a decade or so a new school of thought can be established by the selection of appropriate candidates for Chairs which have fallen vacant during that period. The same end can be advanced even more effectively by the setting up of new Chairs.[43]

Although Polanyi does not explicitly argue that the chief Influentials represent men at outstanding universities and research laboratories, the inference — for anyone acquainted with the sci-

[43] Michael Polanyi, *The Logic of Liberty* (Chicago: University of Chicago Press, 1951), p. 54.

entific community — hardly needs to be made. As a mathematical physicist put it:

> I am constantly amazed at people who recoil from the notion of a scientific establishment. There is no doubt that one exists. In my field its representatives are to be found at Harvard, Berkeley, Illinois, Chicago, the University of California at La Jolla, and the Bell Laboratories.

A similar point is made by Fred Reif and Anselm Strauss in reviewing the career opportunities available to young scientists. Part of their argument emphasizes the importance of a "career escalator" that both begins and ends in the major universities.

> [A young scientist's] awareness of this state of affairs is accentuated by the knowledge that there exists a relatively small elite group of scientists who are responsible for most significant advances in his field and who command an accordingly disproportionate amount of prestige. . . . there also exist well-defined expectations as to the level of accomplishment deemed appropriate at various age levels. The scientist must, therefore, meet these demands at the appropriate points in his career. Once he gets off the career escalator, he may miss opportunities which are available only at certain critical stages and without which it may prove difficult to scramble back onto the escalator.
>
> The young scientist thus runs a real risk of getting started on the wrong foot or of getting out of step with career demands. He may do his graduate work in a second rate department and thereby diminish his chances for top positions. He may, even in an excellent department, choose his field of research unwisely, such as one which is falling out of fashion.[44]

Reinforcing the influence exercised by preeminent institutions in science are networks of informal relations that have an elitist bias. These are initially generated in graduate school from friendship or study groups and are eventually expanded to include the working acquaintances of supervising professors (which extends to their former students), postdoctoral colleagues, and colloquia

---

[44] Fred Reif and Anselm Strauss, "The Impact of Rapid Discovery upon the Scientist's Career," *Social Problems* 12, no. 3 (Winter 1965): 300–301.

"contacts." Ziman has clearly summed up the intricate nature of this system in the following passage:

> How, for example, does one become accepted as a charter member of an Invisible College? It is not sufficient merely to be doing research in that field, or to publish a paper on it, unless this is of such extraordinary merit as to catch the attention of the whole community. The usual entry is achieved by patronage. The students of a particular professor are recommended to his colleagues not merely for jobs, but as potentially able contributors to the field. To have taken one's doctorate in some famous school of research provides one with a ticket of admission, as a visitor or temporary research worker, to another distinguished group, where one's name will then become known. A joint paper with a leading scholar may be mainly the work of the student — but the name upon it may provide the necessary *cachet* for his further advancement.
>
> It is very important to meet people, and be met by them. One of the main functions of colloquia and seminars, where distinguished speakers are invited from other universities to talk about their work, is to clothe abstract personal names with flesh and blood, so that the young research worker may become familiar with the senior members of the College to which he will belong, and may even have a chance to be introduced, and talk informally about his own research work, so that he will be remembered and recognized in the future.[45]

Informal circles of acquaintanceship and personal contact provide a communication system vital to the rapid development of science. But it is through the professional journals — the formal publication machinery of a discipline — that scientific work is officially recognized and the names of authors embedded in the literature surrounding a particular subject. The published work of a scientist is thus important not only because of what it may contribute to scientific perceptions, but because it is an essential link in the professional evaluation of individual performance. A scientist may be brilliant and motivated to explore the secrets of nature, but unless he puts his work in published form, his efforts will be suspect. Publication represents the seal of professional

---

[45] Ziman, *Public Knowledge*, pp. 131–132.

authenticity without which no piece of research can claim to be valid. Again, Ziman has caught the significance of scholarly articles as an index to the authority relations in science.

> An article in a reputable journal does not merely represent the opinions of its author; it bears the *imprimatur* of scientific authenticity, as given to it by the editor and the referees whom he may have consulted.
>
> The referee is the lynchpin about which the whole business of Science is pivoted. His job is simply to report, as an expert, on the value of a paper submitted to a journal. He must say whether the results claimed are of scientific interest, whether they are authenticated and made credible by sound experimental methods and good logic, whether the paper is well expressed, not too cryptic nor too verbose, with adequate references, etc. He reports to the editor, and although this report may be sent to the author for action or rebuttal, he is protected by anonymity.
>
> . . . Again, the business of refereeing is spread over the whole body of active scientists in the particular field covered by the journal. It is true that the more senior persons may be consulted more often, but they have no exclusive privilege in the matter, and are always happier to let the work be done by their junior colleagues. They are not, therefore, obstinate tyrants, to be placated; although each referee may have his own personal standards as an author, he usually accepts the general criteria of the journal to which he is reporting. A consensus as to what constitutes "publishable" work is established, and referees who are persistently too harsh are dropped from the list.[46]

Ziman's argument is quite subtle in depicting the selection of journal referees, but if read carefully, his statement does reflect what takes place. The field from which referees are recruited is not the broad compass of all scientists within a particular discipline. Rather it is a much smaller group of "active scientists" from similar educational backgrounds, circles of acquaintance, and research interests. The editors of professional journals, whose business it is to know where the most "active" work is being done and by whom, perform the specific task of designating referees. In fact, their continued success as editors is likely to

[46] *Ibid.*, pp. 111–113.

depend upon their ability to discharge this function with skill and reliability. Not surprisingly, then, they turn to men whose past contributions to scientific literature qualify them as competent representatives of professional opinion.

Lending additional credence to the theme that the scientific community reflects the activities of professional elites is Harriet Zuckerman's excellent analysis of the sociology of Nobel prizes. Her study points out that within the United States the Nobel awards — which represent the highest recognition given for scientific research — have a peculiar history of being offered to scientists who took their doctorates from, or who were employed by, only five universities. Here is a summary statement of her findings:

> American laureates' careers, from the time of their graduate work through the academic year 1966–67, have seen them affiliated at one time or another with 29 universities, three industrial laboratories, two institutes, one clinic, and one foundation. The top five organizations, among them, have educated or employed more laureates-to-be and laureates than the other 31 combined.[47]

As Table 4.5 reveals, the five universities that have trained and given research opportunities to more laureates and laureates-to-be than all other scientific institutions in the United States are: Harvard, Columbia, the University of California (Berkeley), the University of Chicago, and the California Institute of Technology. Moreover, as Zuckerman suggests, scientists within these institutions generate the standards of training, evaluation, and research performance characteristic of the "upper ranges" of scientific competence.[48]

The thrust of the argument thus far has been that the social organization of science is elitist in character — that the scope of significant decision-making is usually reserved to a small group of scientists who are considered *active* in a field or discipline. Precisely these scientists manipulate the flow of *acceptable* information and therefore control the supply of *legitimate* percep-

[47] Harriet Zuckerman, "The Sociology of the Nobel Prizes," *Scientific American* 217, no. 5 (November 1967): 31.
[48] *Ibid.*, p. 33.

tions within a profession. The techniques and sanctions employed to this end constitute the politics of science and are essential mechanisms for creating support for research traditions. As methods of manipulation, these devices function to exclude perceptions that are suspect (or of doubtful validity) from the *public* realm of scientific discussion and investigation. Thus, one may suppose through nonpublication of controversial ideas, nondiscussion of conflicting evidence, nonappointment or nonpromotion of scientists doing weird or abnormal research, repression of professional honors and awards, denial of research subsidies or grants, and refusal of testing facilities or unique pieces of equipment, the politics of science serves to allocate research priorities and extend the perceptive network of science into areas likely to produce the most significant results.[49]

In coordinating reliable perceptions, the politics of science conditions each scientist's research performance and limits his professional curiosity by filtering both through a grid of collegial criticism and control. Moreover, through the use of a variety of manipulative techniques and sanctions, it directs scientific attention and energy to puzzle-solving routines that could scarcely be as specialized and efficient under any other system.[50]

Such a view of politics in science is rather unconventional, for scientists do not, as a rule, think of social structures and processes as being directly related to scientific perception. The conventional reaction is one equating perception with an "inner show"

---

[49] The first four sanctions are mentioned by Alfred de Grazia, *et al.*, eds., *The Velikovsky Affair*, p. 201.

[50] Thomas Kuhn puts the matter this way:

> The areas investigated by normal science are, of course, miniscule; the enterprise now under discussion has drastically restricted vision. But those restrictions, born from confidence in a paradigm, turn out to be essential to the development of science. By focusing attention upon a small range of relatively esoteric problems, the paradigm forces scientists to investigate some part of nature in a detail and depth that would otherwise be unimaginable. . . . During the period when the paradigm is successful, the profession will have solved problems that its members could scarcely have imagined and would never have undertaken without commitment to the paradigm.

Kuhn, *The Structure of Scientific Revolutions*, pp. 24–25.

Table 4.5 Ameriican Nobel Laureates and Their University
Affiliations through the Academic Year 1966–67

Institution	Laureates Affiliated as Recipients of Doctoral Degree	Laureates Doing Prize- Winning Work at Institution	Laureates Affiliated at Time of Award	Laureates Currently Active on Staff
Harvard University	11	13	13	7
Columbia University	8	9	7	2
University of California at Berkeley	6	7	8	8
University of Chicago	4	6	4	2
California Institute of Technology	4	3	7	3
Princeton University	6	1	1	1
Washington University		6	3	1
Johns Hopkins University	5			
Bell Telephone Laboratories		4	2	1
Stanford University		4	4	5
Cornell University	1	2	2	1
University of Rochester	2	1	1	
Rockefeller University		3	7	2
University of Illinois	2		1	1
Massachusetts Institute of Technology	2		1	
Mayo Clinic		2	2	
University of Minnesota	2			
University of Wisconsin	1	1	1	
Yale University	2			2
Case Institute of Technology		1		
General Electric Research Laboratory		1	1	
University of Indiana	1		1	
Institute for Advanced Study		1	1	

Table 4.5 (*continued*)

Institution	Laureates Affiliated as Recipients of Doctoral Degree	Laureates Doing Prize-Winning Work at Institution	Laureates Affiliated at Time of Award	Laureates Currently Active on Staff
University of Michigan		I		
New York University		I	I	I
University of Pittsburgh	I			
Rockefeller Foundation		I		
Rutgers University		I	I	
St. Louis University		I	I	
University of Texas		I		
University of California at Los Angeles			I	I
University of California at San Diego			I	I
Western Reserve University			I	I
Beckman Instruments			I	
Carnegie Institution of Washington			I	
State University of New York at Stony Brook				I

Source: From Harriet Zuckerman, "The Sociology of the Nobel Prizes," *Scientific American* 217, no. 5 (November 1967): 31.

that takes place within the scientist himself. As a prominent physicist explains it:

> While man's scientific instruments do constitute, as we have seen, an effective extension of his body and his sense organs, there are no comparable *external* structures that substitute for the *inward* side of the perceptive process. . . . Thus, it is up to the *scientist himself* to be aware of contradictions between his hypotheses and what he observes, to be sensitive to new relationships in what he observes, and to put forth conjectures or hypotheses, which

explain the known facts, embodying these new relationships, and have additional implications with regard to what is as yet unknown, so that they can be tested in further experiments and observations. So there is always finally a stage where an *essen-tially perceptual process* is needed in scientific research — a process taking place within the scientist himself.[51]

I have tried to suggest that this notion is too limited, for it denies the existence of external influences that substantively affect decisions (1) about what paradigms or theories will prevail, (2) what areas are to be researched, and (3) the degree of confidence or reliability attributed to particular research techniques.

The perceptual process is a function of the interaction between the individual scientist and the community of science practitioners. But it is specifically focused and articulated by political mechanisms that permit the resolution of disagreements and conflicts without destroying the vital bond holding the scientific community together — the quest for a reliable, systematic expression of reality.

THE EMERGENCE AND RESOLUTION OF SCIENTIFIC DISPUTES

The politics of science is most clearly visible under the conditions of extreme conflict — where competing paradigms or theories appear irreconcilable — but it is present in less obtrusive patterns at all levels of inquiry. Since conflicts may vary sharply in terms of size, intensity, and complexity, it is useful to establish a continuum of conflict-dimensions before moving into a discussion of specific disputes. Under hypothetical conditions of normal science (see Table 4.6), empirical disciplines with a high degree of theoretical unity tend to be characterized by small-scale conflicts, usually highly technical and restricted in nature. (Perhaps a serviceable example of this kind of conflict is the current disagreement in physics over the possibility of using flames as sound recorders and amplifiers.[52] Neither party to the

[51] David Bohm, *The Special Theory of Relativity* (New York: W. A. Benjamin, 1965), p. 226.

[52] See *Nature* 219 (August 24, 1968): 849–850.

Table 4.6 PATTERNS OF THEORETICAL CONFLICT AND REGIME TYPES
UNDER CONDITIONS OF NORMAL EMPIRICAL SCIENCE

Scope of Conflict		
Micro	*Meso*	*Macro*
Physics Astronomy Chemistry	Biology Geology	Parapsychology
	Regime Type	
Oligarchy	Competitive Plurality	Democracy

dispute believes that it is impossible *in principle* for flame radiation to be used as a recording medium. Rather the conflict is over techniques for measuring and controlling flame luminosity and sound production.) In contrast, empirical disciplines with intermediate or poorly developed theories are victimized by conflicts considerably more fundamental and much more prolonged. Typical of the disputes that can emerge within this dimension are those in biology dividing the field, in the words of a Harvard paleontologist, "into physical, chemical, or molecular biology on the one hand and organismal or evolutionary biology on the other." [53] Yet even within these two branches there are disputes of rather basic importance, such as the current one in molecular biology that questions whether DNA is a self-replicating genetic material.[54] In geology, too, conflicts question the foundation of established positions, such as Gilvarry's theory that the ocean basins of the earth were formed by the impact of meteorites before the continents existed,[55] or Wegener's theory of continental

[53] George G. Simpson, "The Crisis in Biology," *The American Scholar* 36 (1966–67): 363.

[54] See Barry Commoner, *Science and Survival* (New York: Viking Press, 1966).

[55] For a discussion of John J. Gilvarry's theory, see John Lear, "When Is a New Idea Fit to Print," *Saturday Review* 45, no. 14 (April 7, 1962): 41–45.

drift, which suggests that the present location of the continents is due to sea-floor spreading.[56]

Within highly developed empirical disciplines, conflicts large enough to produce theoretical revolutions are not common occurrences. They are extraordinary and monumental, for the crises they provoke are the force behind the great paradigm shifts of science. In the early twentieth century the revolutions associated with such theories as relativity and quantum mechanics represent conflicts of this order. The revolutionary crises created by these conditions begin, as Kuhn has pointed out, "with the blurring of a paradigm and the consequent loosening of the rules for normal research. . . . And all crises close with the emergence of a new candidate for paradigm and with the subsequent battle over its acceptance." [57] Even though the resolution of paradigm conflicts provides an unusual opportunity to see the politics of science from exaggerated dimensions, few, if any, studies have been directed to this end. The techniques of interpersonal adjustment and manipulation surrounding these events must therefore be inferred from sketchy historical accounts. Interestingly, at this level of conflict one can sometimes learn a great deal from unsuccessful challenges to existing paradigms or from the reaction of scientists to theories they regard as distinctly unscientific.

Unlike empirical disciplines, under either normal or extraordinary conditions, the formal sciences are not forced to create theories that conform to happenings in the "observable" world.[58] Formal scientists are at liberty to construct alternative theories, providing their work employs the universal standards of mathematical proof. In discussing scientific disputes it is necessary to treat the formal sciences somewhat differently, since the foundation of their theoretical systems is not empirically oriented. The following analysis concentrates on conflicts in mathematics as matters of individual taste or style, rather than as issues growing

[56] For a recent argument in favor of continental drift, see Patrick M. Hurley, "The Confirmation of Continental Drift," *Scientific American* 218, no. 4 (April 1968): 53–64.

[57] Kuhn, *The Structure of Scientific Revolutions*, p. 84.

[58] See Hagstrom, *The Scientific Community*, p. 276.

out of competing theories or schools of thought. The remainder of the exercise focuses upon the emergence and resolution of specific disputes in molecular biology, geology, and particle physics. In molecular biology the emphasis is on the current debate about the structure of cell membranes, while in geology and physics it is on Gilvarry's theory of ocean basins and the challenge posed to quantum mechanics by the "hidden"-variable theory.

Conflict in Mathematics. Since mathematics rests upon universally accepted criteria of proof, its controversies tend to cluster around what constitutes important areas of research rather than questions that focus upon the foundations of a subject or the validity of mathematical methods. Consequently, mathematical conflicts are largely matters of aesthetic preference or style. This does not mean that they are characterized by amity; on the contrary, stylistic disputes can be both professionally vicious and personally devastating.

In statistics, questions of style are sometimes replaced by more fundamental disputes, but the issues raised do not question the standards of mathematical correctness. Instead they arise from the close association of statistics with empirical science. Here foreign, extramathematical considerations are introduced by different approaches to the analysis of empirical data. Although empirical studies may be converted into correct mathematical systems, the controversy over the approach may remain. Two of Hagstrom's interviews illustrate aspects of this conflict.

> A man wrote a number of articles on an issue, and the statisticians at X university didn't like them, and he probably couldn't get a job there because of them. But then what better way is there of judging a man than by his published work?

> Sir Ronald Fisher is a querulous individual who was also a revolutionary. His revolution started in 1915. . . . At that time Pearson was authoritarian; he was editor of the only journal and the director of a unique laboratory. He published Fisher's first paper but thereafter tried to stop him at every turn. As a result, Fisher developed an inferiority complex. He divided the world into pro- and anti-Fisher segments. He resisted any thinking against

his points of view. . . . At first *Biometrika* was the only journal
and it was controlled by one Karl Pearson who was not a nice
man. And Fisher had a spectacular struggle with Pearson. . . .
He acquired power after Karl Pearson's death. . . . Fisher became a Fellow of the Royal Society, did a great deal of applied
work, and helped others. As a result, up to now only members
of Fisher's monastery can be elected to the Royal Society. This
is one facet of his power; membership in the Royal Society is
very important to English scientists.[59]

Although disagreements in statistics may reveal keen rivalry
due to methodological differences, the larger part of mathematics
(which is nonempirically oriented) is immune from this struggle.
A young and promising mathematician was asked why "matters
of style" are more characteristic of mathematical disputes than
"matters of method." His response was lengthy, but it deserves
to be quoted in full.

There are wide differences of opinion among mathematicians
concerning the preferable "style" or type of mathematical work.
These differences concern primarily (a) the degree of abstraction desirable and (closely related) (b) the degree of motivation
by and impact on "applications." Thus the currently glamorous
field of algebraic topology, differential geometry and functional
analysis tend to be highly abstract and to concentrate on problems whose roots are in the abstract formulation itself. On the
other hand, fields such as probability theory, differential equations and celestial mechanics deal with more "concrete" objects
(at least they seem concrete to mathematicians) and focus on
problems which have roots in empirical science. It should be said
immediately that it is not fashionable for the mathematician to
be overly interested in empirical problems per se; but standard
types of problems in "classical" fields are often founded in empirical work.

   *These differences in style lead to considerable verbal sniping,
but not to any serious rifts in the mathematical community.* There
are several reasons for this. The first is historical: mathematical
abstraction typically begins by attempting to work abstractly
with properties common to several concrete mathematical sys-

[59] *Ibid.*, p. 269.

tems, and has therefore constantly yielded new results in concrete situations. Elementary examples are the Greek problems of trisecting an angle or squaring a circle with ruler and compass. The impossibility of such constructions was first proved in the nineteenth century by using the theory of groups, a seemingly unrelated abstraction. The power of abstract methods is therefore almost universally appreciated, and mathematics as a whole grows constantly more abstract. Yet most mathematicians seem also to retain a sense of the history of their discipline, and to recognize that, of the infinite number of abstract structures, only those which have roots in more concrete areas of mathematics are sufficiently "fruitful" to be worth investigating.

Secondly, and perhaps more important, is the general agreement on what constitutes valid mathematics. Controversies concerning the foundations of a subject and the validity of the methods used tend to be sharper than disagreements over what constitutes important research. Mathematics currently lacks widespread foundational controversies among working mathematicians. The last serious fight over methodology concerned the transfinite methods of Georg Cantor (late nineteenth century). Still, the foundations of mathematics are by no means philosophically secure: there is currently no generally accepted philosophy of mathematics, and one school (the intuitionists) rejects many universally used methods of proof on philosophical grounds. But these controversies are steadfastly ignored by working mathematicians. Mathematics has, after all, been a going concern since the Greeks, and if the philosophers can't analyze it, that's their problem. Agreement on what is *correct* is universal among mathematicians.

A third factor, which mitigates the effects of disagreements over style, is the breadth of the field. It is sometimes said that physics, for example, tends to concentrate its efforts on one area at a time. Mathematics has no such tendency. This has the important consequence that a man's mathematical work tends to be judged by others who share his taste. There are several reasons for this, the most important being that a topologist can barely comprehend a research paper by a classical function theorist and vice versa. In other words, *all* mathematicians have a restricted domain of competence within a huge field. Thus the leading general mathematical journals have associate editors in widely different subjects, who refer submitted papers in their subject to like-minded referees. The better departments of mathematics also contain scholars of quite diverse interests, who generally cannot comprehend the research of those in other fields.

Finally, there are journals devoted solely to individual fields within mathematics which maintain the style of the field. (There are over 300 mathematical journals.) This diversity is thought desirable, and does not destroy the feeling of belonging to a common profession. I should reiterate that this is possible because all fields share a common standard of mathematical proof.

From this interview "matters of style" emerge as the most important determinants within the field of mathematics. As the interview also indicates, stylistic possibilities are limited by three factors: a sense of mathematical history, universal agreement over what constitutes valid mathematical proof, and the breadth of mathematical interest and specialization itself. Such factors help shield the substantive concerns of mathematicians from the charge that they are mere crystallizations of collective taste, respectable for the moment but not necessarily of enduring value. Yet it should be pointed out that these checks have long-range significance and are not immediately instrumental in the determination of mathematical interests.

Decisions affecting the choice of mathematical specialization, and perhaps ultimately the prestige of the mathematician himself, are influenced by interpersonal processes of much shorter duration. The processes that matter here involve a *political* estimate of three contingencies: what fields have the greatest growth potential, what alternate competences should be maintained as a hedge against mathematical obsolescence, and what specific subjects are most likely to be regarded as nontrivial and interesting. To some degree each mathematician must map his career strategy in response to these possibilities. Several of Hagstrom's interviews reveal how candid mathematicians can be in talking about these problems.

> At the turn of the century, a hot area in mathematics was the so-called theory of geometrical invariance. At the time, the notion of invariance was recognized as unifying a great many geometrical ideas. So there was an enormous study of invariance at the time. It was a fairly technical and fairly narrow area, and a

lot of Ph.D.'s were being turned out at the time in the theory of invariance. Well, this went on for a time, and pretty soon they exhausted almost everything that could be said; the field wasn't closed, there were still a great many things to be done, but it was generally realized that what you were going to say would be more of the same kind of thing. It really wasn't going to bring entirely new ideas into the field. I've known a good many mathematicians, now all in their sixties, who were trained in this field, did their research in the area for many years, and didn't learn any of the related mathematics at the time. When the popularity of invariance theory went down they were simply left stranded. For example, they had difficulty getting papers published, because editors were just not interested in the material. So that they were perfectly aware that the field had passed them by, and they eventually gave up doing research. They felt they were too old to branch out into new fields and it was as plain as could be that it was impossible for them to receive recognition for research in what they had done. Obviously they were quite discouraged and frustrated.

I'll stay in topology as long as I can do something. If I couldn't, I wouldn't stay in mathematics, I wouldn't want to. I might go into industry or another science. One's learning ability does drop off with age. This doesn't hurt in one's own field because although your ability drops your knowledge increases and you can still do very good work. . . . Short bursts of explosive energy are required in mathematical research. When one is old he is unable to do this — say after fifty. In my middle forties I might not feel happy staying in the subject. It may depend on how well I can do in developing students.[60]

Career strategies, of course, are never fully planned in advance. They represent incremental adjustments to anticipated conditions within the professional world of mathematics. Information about the state of the field (which is essential to an estimate of its possibilities) is an inherent part of such activities as private correspondence, professional conferences or meetings, sabbatical leaves, consulting visits, special seminars, and the "rumor mill." At bottom, then, the role of politics in mathematical controversies differs from that of the empirical sciences. Unlike empirical dis-

[60] *Ibid.*, pp. 233–234.

ciplines the political aspects of mathematical disputes do not affect the perceptive capacity of mathematicians to determine either valid criteria of proof or what model best describes physical reality. Rather they affect matters of secondary importance such as the choice of mathematical fields, whether one's work is regarded as trivial or interesting, and the extent to which one develops related or peripheral competences throughout his productive years.

Conflict in Molecular Biology: The Structure of Cell Membranes. While it is perhaps true that some biologists would like to create the impression that scientific disputes within the field are matters of routine decision, this may not be the case. In fact, as biology continues to mature as a discipline, one can expect the emergence of disputes at progressively higher levels of abstraction. The importance of controversies of this nature is that they are not likely to be resolved by an appeal to evidence alone. Hence, the success or failure of a model may depend upon the kind of support it can enlist. David Green, who is a participant in the following discussion, has described conditions in molecular biology that appear susceptible to this interpretation:

> Until a few years ago the conceptual framework in the field of mitochondrial structure and function played a relatively minor role in determining the direction and in shaping the design of experimentation. In the phase of describing phenomena, the conceptual framework is not crucial. It is only when experimentation reaches the interpretative and explanatory stages that permissiveness or indifference with respect to the conceptual framework has consequences which inhibit progress.
>
> Within a relatively short time . . . the study of the mitochondrion has been drastically altered. The concept of what is a membrane underlies the concept of what is a complex of the electron transfer chain. . . . This pyramiding of new concepts has created the need for a delineation of the conceptual framework within which current research on mitochondria is progressing.[61]

---

[61] David Green and David H. MacLennan, "The Structure and Function of the Mitochondrial Cristael Membrane," *Bioscience* 19, no. 3 (March 1969): 213.

The controversy with which Green is associated concerns membrane structure in cells and is one of the most intense disputes in biology today. In essence, the conflict centers around the "subject of biological energy transduction. That is, how chemical energy can actually perform physical work in the cell — like moving molecules through membranes." [62] The prospect of a hardbitten scientific controversy led to interviews concerning the political nature of the matter with biologists in the field. The flavor of these exchanges may be summarized by reporting the response of a participant in the debate; to prevent his remarks from injuring scientific reputations, the names of the parties involved are changed.

The whole dispute which surrounds the nature of membrane structure has most interesting aspects which can be seen under the surface.

The Traditionalists: D. J. Foster is defending his unit membrane concept proposed in 1959 based on the Dentler-Downs model of 1935.

The Powerful Outsiders are represented by those who are now invading the field with queer ideas (which are probably the basis for a new model): for example, D. B. Brown and his structural protein model (1961). (Brown uses symposia on other subjects to inject his ideas.)

The "Modern Technique" people are those who disdain traditional studies like D. J. Foster and his EM (electron microscopy) and use only high-class new methods such as optical rotatory dispersion and circular dichroism and spectral analysis to study protein lipid association in membranes. They say that Foster is wrong and, ironically, return to the concepts of Livingston (1933), although they do not refer to him. This group is represented by Rye, Jones, and Smith.

The Broker function is performed by those who collect various new ideas and draw models without doing any major experiments on their own. They also arrange symposia where they make major theoretical pronouncements. Art Black is a good example here. Notice how he blankets the literature with his story. Take a look at his latest article and note the list of references to him-

[62] Robert Bernhard, "On the Road with David Green — Campaigning for a New Theory," *Scientific Research,* May 13, 1968, p. 33.

self. There is also Caravan, who is an unsuccessful broker because he didn't get enough papers out.

The Traditional Followers are men like Whiteway, who got X-ray diffraction patterns out of myelin, which confirmed Foster's view, but couldn't get proper patterns out of other membranes. Whiteway keeps trying to think of another interpretation which is now sneaking up on him through the others mentioned above. Bullitt is following along with his new freeze-etch method.

The Modifiers in the struggle are typified by scientists like Sanders (who is mad at Foster because he beat him to the unit membrane). Sanders finds globs in the membrane, which he considers to be lipid globs, thus only modifying the unit membrane concept. He also emphasizes diversity in membranes by keeping the lipid inside. His globs will probably be protein units, but he is slow to make such a drastic change, so others (Brown) beat him to it. It may be that Sanders has no courage. Or it could be that he simply has a restricted imagination.

The Peripheralists: people interested in nerve impulse transmission, salt balance, gasteroenterology, etc., whose theories depend on membrane structure, tend to hang on to old ideas because all their experimental proposals depend on the old idea. The best example is the soap-bubble-model membrane people, who are studying electrical transmission and water transport through soap bubbles because they are models for Foster's unit membrane. If his theory falls, all their experiments lose significance, and they will have to write up new grant requests. For them it is important that the unit membrane concept hold out until their grants run out and they can set up new models based on the new concept. (King, *et al.*)

The Mavericks (nonpowerful outsiders — where "powerful" means those with a large research establishment, editorial positions, etc., usually built up by work in other areas than the one they are invading): these people are those with different ideas who are ignored by the established experts until they make enough noise so that they must be attacked. Note that Farmer and MacDonald have not been referred to by Black, Brown, Foster, Waters, Springer, Banks even after three years. Farmer, *et al.* wrote their own book. I had my evidence for a similar structure rejected by *Science* on the basis that it was not consistent with the well-established Foster unit membrane theory. However, my research was finally published due to the fact that a friend invited me to a symposium he was organizing. It will, of course, be published in other journals (a) where traditionalists are not reviewers of the papers, (b) where I know the editors, (c) where I am an editor, or (d) at any other symposia I can get invited to. If it is not published in four or five places, it can safely be ignored by leaders in the field. If it can't be ignored, then it is important to try to modify the maverick view to look like a modification of the unit membrane theory. I believe that the theory or modification reaches final acceptance when it is incorporated into textbooks. Then it becomes established and subject to attack by new mavericks and outsiders and newer technique people.

One of the contenders in the dispute admitted that the present level of theoretical conflict in biology was unequivocally immersed in the political strategies of personal salesmanship and scientific advertisement. But, he continued:

> To make changes you have to be highly articulate, persuasive, and devastating. You have to go to the heart of the matter. But in doing this you open yourself to attack. I've been called fanatical, paranoid, obsessed . . . , but I'm going to win. Time is on my side.
>
> . . . To return to the matter at hand, take the "Dentler-Downs" model of membrane structure. It has become a kind of religion, although there is not a scrap of evidence for it. The "Dentler-Downs" model is not right, but the problem is how do you get it out of the minds of referees and graduate students. In short, how do you percolate new ideas down into a system where it is a tradition to accept the "Dentler-Downs" model?
>
> And yet, to be altogether honest, one must recognize that the social system of biological science is not entirely closed. There is still a certain diversity of interest. But the point is that if the "Dentler-Downs" model goes, lots of previous work and reputations go with it. We've been at it now for three or four years, and there is evidence now that opposition is not so entrenched.

A membraneologist who is unsympathetic to the above respondent had this to say about his comments on "biological politics":

> We all, of course, recognize that there is a certain inexactness in biological knowledge. But [his] trouble is not *all* political. He based his theory solely upon electron microscopy. This is risky

business, to say the least. The tissue to be photographed must be dead and elaborately stained before its image can be captured. Obviously the possibility of undesirable artifacts is frightening. [He] himself mentioned in 1965 that the reality of his model was not in question, but that the size and form certainly were.

However, aside from the technical difficulties that attend his theory, [he] himself must be held responsible for some of his "selling" problems. Labelled by a colleague of mine as "insulting," [he] indeed hardly possesses the patience necessary for the presentation of his theories. In sum, [he] is in a difficult position. He fights against professional inertia, an unpleasing personal image, and a group of well-established scientists – all with an experimental approach which is limited in scope and result. [He] suffers not so much from a repressive oligarchy bent on his destruction, as from a plurality of opponents, some of whom like the idea of a revised membrane model, but who detest the man who is responsible for its initial formulation.

Another biologist from the same department added further information about the contender's political position within the professional circles of biologists.

[He] is not in with the boys who dominate the prestigious journals – although he now edits a journal himself. The reason for this is simple: he has a malicious personality. He tends to think views not in agreement with his own are wrong. This has had certain unfortunate consequences. He now appears to be frozen out of most foundation selection committees. But even so, he somehow maintains contact with the National Heart Institute. Funds from this organization enable him to keep a stable of about twenty post-docs who pour out the data. He can therefore keep abreast of the latest developments by allocating work loads among his "stable help." This frees him to do innovative work of his own.

Although the dispute over membrane structure has not yet been resolved, it is not the kind of controversy that has no foreseeable end. With the emergence of better techniques of research, the dispute will subside, and its "residue" will ultimately find its way into the textbooks of the field. At this level, students will perhaps be introduced to the material without the slightest indication that it was once part of an exciting struggle within the discipline. As a consequence, perhaps another generation of scientists will be led to believe that the empirical enterprise is immune to interpersonal movement and conflict. Thomas Kuhn illustrates this point with care:

> There are no collections of "Readings" in the natural sciences. Nor is the science student encouraged to read the historical classics of his field — works in which he might discover other ways of regarding the problems discussed in his text, but in which he would also meet problems, concepts, and standards of solution that his future profession has long since discarded and replaced.

> Even books that compete for adoption in a single course differ mainly in level and in pedogogic detail, not in substance or conceptual structure. Last, but most important of all, is the characteristic technique of textbook presentation. Except in their occasional introductions, science textbooks do not describe the sorts of problems that the professional may be asked to solve and the variety of techniques available for their solution. Rather these books exhibit concrete problem-solutions that the professional has come to accept as paradigms. . . .[63]

Yet, regardless of the form in which cell membranes are passed on to the following generation, an examination of the major participants' positions in the struggle reveals the role politics plays in extending scientific perception. Behind the published results that technically outline controversies are such political maneuvers as marketing, salesmanship, and manipulation — all of which are vital to scientific inquiry. The present case has drawn attention to four strategies: the use of research techniques that are widely accepted, the cultivation of an active research clientele, the control of a collegial competition, and the refinement of such conciliatory virtues as intellectual poise and good manners.

Conflict in Geology: The Formation of the Ocean Basins. Scientific controversies in geology are similar to those in biology,

[63] Thomas Kuhn, "The Essential Tension: Tradition and Innovation in Scientific Research," in Calvin W. Taylor and Frank Barron, eds., *Scientific Creativity: Its Recognition and Development* (New York: Wiley, 1963), pp. 341–354. Quoted in Hagstrom, *The Scientific Community*, p. 10.

for both disciplines lie in the intermediate range of theoretical unification, and both have decisional structures controlled by proximate elites.

Moreover, many disputes in geology can produce waves of interest that move beyond the professional concerns of geologists into the less carefully guarded magazines of the popular press. When this occurs, political tactics achieve a visibility that under normal circumstances would be difficult to detect. Even when the visibility is increased, the role of politics in scientific perception can still be overlooked. The lay public, for example, sometimes believes that scientists respond to an unorthodox theory with partiality and prejudice – and are guilty of violating the rigid code of scientific methodology. The scientists, on the other hand, are disturbed when an uninformed public considers itself capable of weighing the scientific evidence in question. What is perhaps tragic is that both groups seem either unwilling or unable to appreciate the importance of conflict in science and the desirability of political techniques as perceptual tools.

The recent dispute over Gilvarry's theory of the formation of ocean basins strikingly illustrates these themes. In 1961 John J. Gilvarry wrote an article for the *Saturday Review* entitled, "How the Sky Drove the Land from the Bottom of the Sea." [64] The major point of Gilvarry's argument was that the ocean basins of the earth were formed by the exploding force of meteorites billions of years ago – long before the continents existed. This was a dramatic hypothesis and one with immense public appeal. Six months after its publication, seven scientists from the University of California (La Jolla) delivered a blistering attack not only against the plausibility of the theory and the scientific competence of its author, but against the *Saturday Review* for failing to have the article examined by specialists in the field. Here is a nontechnical sample of the criticism:

> There are so many serious problems entirely neglected by Dr. Gilvarry, so many over-simplified facts and even cases of misinterpreted data, that his speculations are unacceptable to most if

[64] *Saturday Review* 44, no. 44 (November 4, 1961): 53–58.

not all competent students of the origin and history of the earth.

If this is indeed the case . . . then it is clear that this article would be just bad "education" to an uninformed reader. No scientist can face with equanimity the prospect of misrepresenting either the theories of science or the methods by which new hypotheses are tested and finally accepted or rejected. Certainly to publish such misrepresentations on a very large scale, as in the *Saturday Review*, is to provide the general public with an erroneous impression of scientists and the scientific method. We feel sure that you would deplore such a result at least as much as we do.

. . . Dr. Gilvarry's speculations do not deserve the label of "science." Of course, we realize that the prior publication of these ideas in a reputable scientific journal, *Nature*, absolves you of much of the responsibility for a critical review of their validity. . . . However, we suggest that it is most unwise to assume that anything published in a scientific journal is "good science." Due in part to the increased difficulty of coping with the flood of scientific papers and of communications between specialists in various fields, it has become more and more necessary to examine *critically* all papers purporting to be scientific in scope and purpose. We earnestly recommend that you do so, if necessary with the aid and advice of specialists in the fields discussed, in the future.[65]

The response of the science editor of *Saturday Review* was predictable and once again focuses attention upon how laymen regard the activities of science.

As the stated objective of the authors of this letter is avoidance of "bad education . . . [of] an uninformed reader," any reasonable response to their complaint must adopt the form of an educational exercise. First must come the inquiry:

What is science?

Science is the impartial study of verifiable phenomena. . . .[66]

Like the science editor, the lay public regards suppression of theoretical unorthodoxies as unjust and unscientific. More than

[65] *Saturday Review* 45, no. 14 (April 7, 1962): 42–43.
[66] *Ibid.*, p. 41.

that, they recoil in anger and amazement when they learn that scientists actually discriminate against novel theories on grounds that seem beyond the pale of evidentiary inference.

Conflict in Physics: The Attack against Quantum Mechanics. Within established scientific disciplines, attempts to challenge prevailing theories can be met with prolonged and determined resistance. Take, for example, the relatively persistent controversy in physics between advocates of quantum and "subquantum" mechanics. Stated simply, the essence of the dispute lies in a fundamental disagreement over the internal behavior of the atom and the nature of matter. According to quantum mechanics, atomic systems (particles, atoms or molecules) are not part of an autonomous universe of cause-and-effect events. Quanta of radiant energy have no external, representational characteristics; instead, they are defined by the results of physical measurements.

> Some types of experiments determine the behavior of large numbers of similar systems, and the measurements therefore reflect the behavior of the individual systems only in a statistical way. Other types of experiments, in which cloud chambers, bubble chambers, photographic emulsions and counters play a part, determine the behavior of individual systems directly, and a large number of measurements on similar systems have to be made to obtain statistically significant results. The predictions of quantum mechanics are therefore concerned with specifying the possible results of a measurement, and the probability that any one of these results will be obtained.[67]

The quantum world is an artificial reconstruction of experimental probabilities. Without the tinkering that "experimentalists do with particles, the particles would have no properties at all . . . [their] . . . only mode of being is to be observed." [68] In con-

[67] Herbert S. Green, *Matrix Mechanics* (Groningen: P. Noordhoff Ltd., 1965) p. 8.

[68] Robert Bernhard, "Skeleton in the Closet of Physics: Whatever Became of Reality?" *Scientific Research* 3, no. 3 (February 5, 1968): 30. His quotations here and elsewhere in the text are reprinted by permission of the publisher.

trast, subquantum theory suggests that there may be a concealed stratum of atomic phenomena which is not observation-dependent and which conforms to the classical laws of determinism. If somehow its "hidden" variables can be specified, quantum mechanics may be freed from its probabilistic structure and its events explained in terms of causal laws.

The theoretical foundation of quantum mechanics is based on two key assumptions: Heisenberg's uncertainty principle and Bohr's principle of complementarity. As Robert Bernhard has explained:

> Uncertainty originated in the admonition that the simplest act of measurement — and all scientific observation can be reduced to acts of measurement — always sufficiently disturbs the process being studied to introduce an irreducible degree of vagary as to its true qualities. And complementarity explained the empirical fact that units of matter are sometimes wavelike and at other times like corpuscular bodies — so they must be both. The traditional explanation of uncertainty states that to measure accurately the velocity, q, of a particle, a short wave-length X-ray is required; but the particle recoils from the impinging ray, producing an unpredictable effect on its momentum, p. So the observation of q induces an unavoidable error in p, and *vice versa*.[69]

The uncertainty principle is further reinforced by the von Neumann theorem which proves mathematically "that no previously unknown factors . . . [can] . . . ever be introduced to help define a system more precisely than is possible in quantum mechanics." [70] In theoretical terms this means that "hidden" variables cannot be "discovered" at some point which would yield precise enough measurements to contradict the laws of probability and reinstate deterministic relationships.

The opposition to the statistical character of quantum theory and its implication for the structure and movement of matter is not a freshly mounted attack. It has cropped up several times over the last forty years, but it has never met with widespread interest or enthusiasm. Albert Einstein, who was part of an earlier

[69] *Ibid.*
[70] *Ibid.*

version of the controversy, left this impression of what it was like to endorse an unpopular theory.

> What does not satisfy me in that theory [quantum mechanics], from the standpoint of principle, is its attitude towards that which appears to me to be the programmatic aim of all physics: the complete description of any (individual) real situation (as it supposedly exists irrespective of any act of observation or substantiation). Whenever the positivistically inclined modern physicist hears such a formulation his reaction is that of a pitying smile. He says to himself: "there we have the naked formulation of a metaphysical prejudice, empty of content, a prejudice, moreover, the conquest of which constitutes the major epistemological achievement of physicists within the last quarter-century. Has any man ever perceived a "real physical situation?" How is it possible that a reasonable person could today still believe that he can refute our essential knowledge and understanding by drawing up such a bloodless ghost?" [71]

In addition to Einstein, who represented a tradition that began with Planck, resistance to the "uncertainty principle" of quantum theory has been kept alive by Nobelist L. de Broglie, H. Margenau, L. Cohen, and David Bohm.[72] Margenau and Cohen have developed several criticisms of the Heisenberg principle which directly attack the theory's logic. In rather simplified terms, Bernhard briefly summarizes their arguments as follows:

> [First] in its use of terms like "unpredictable," the disturbance theory [i.e., disturbance induced by acts of measurement] has a decidedly classical twist and, if the interpretation is correct, then to be consistent with its view of the particle and the photon (the unit of the X-ray field) as entities interacting in complete classical detail, it should admit the controllability and practicability of the results. Instead, the "disturbance" explanation suddenly surrenders the point at issue: where does the unpredictability come

[71] Paul A. Schlipp, ed., *Albert Einstein: Philosopher-Scientist* (Evanston, Ill.: The Library of Living Philosophers, 1949), p. 667.

[72] For a number of philosophers who take a critical view of the "uncertainty principle" see Mario Bunge, ed., *The Critical Approach to Science and Philosophy* (London: The Free Press of Glencoe, Collier-Macmillan, 1964), especially the essays by Wolfgang Yourgrau and Paul K. Feyerabend.

from? As a concession it calls the interaction "mysterious" and therefore begs the question, since classical electrodynamics is able to provide all the precise answers necessary to determine how the particle is perturbed by the radiation field. [Second] it is widely acknowledged that quantum mechanics is a broader theory than classical physics; classical physics being a limiting case of quantum mechanics when distances and masses get larger. If this is true, then the disturbance theory violates logic, for it uses classical reasoning to make a case for a quantum principle. If the case could be properly made things would be reversed — classical physics would become the wider discipline and quantum mechanics only a limiting case.[73]

Although Margenau and Cohen point up certain logical difficulties within quantum theory, David Bohm argues that the structure of the theory itself prevents the emergence of different (and perhaps more satisfying) interpretations of subatomic reality. His statement of the problem is both clear and penetrating.

It seems, then, that the question of the possibility of hidden variables underlying the quantum theory is still problematic. Besides . . . if the claims based on von Neumann's theorem are accepted as valid then it would follow, from the facts confirming the current quantum theory, that a different general structure of concepts is impossible. Thus, it is made to appear that the linguistic structure of quantum mechanics prevents even the assertion of the *possibility* that the basic postulates underlying the theory may be false.[74]

The central concern behind Bohm's critique is the likelihood that quantum theory may actually hinder a deeper *understanding* of the structure and movement of matter. Although quantum theory provides a useful system of calculation, science, in Bohm's judgment, must ultimately go beyond prediction and application; it

---

[73] Bernhard, "Skeleton in the Closet," pp. 30–31.

[74] D. Bohm and J. Bub, "A Proposed Solution of the Measurement Problem in Quantum Mechanics by a Hidden Variable Theory." *Reviews of Modern Physics* 38, no. 3 (July, 1966): 453. A similar statement can be found in an earlier essay by Bohm, "A Suggested Interpretation of the Quantum Theory in Terms of 'Hidden' Variables, I," *Physical Review*, Vol. 85, no. 2 (January 15, 1952).

must strive to create a unified, coherent understanding of all physical phenomena from the atom to the galaxies. As he explains:

> Of course, a system of calculation of experimental probabilities is useful. Nevertheless, science is surely more than *merely* a set of algorithms for an engineer's handbook. Science also aims at an *understanding* of the over-all structure and order of movement of matter from the atom to the galaxies. While science also has the aim of prediction and useful application, these in themselves cannot correctly be identified with the whole of the act of understanding, in which one grasps the order, the structure of a complex process in a unified coherent set of concepts. . . . the difference between understanding and *mere* prediction can be illustrated by the example of trying to find one's way through a city that one does not know. One may be given directions, which in effect constitute predictions of the order of streets and buildings that one will discover if one walks in certain ways. But a map of the city gives a unified coherent understanding of its over-all order and structure, from which useful predictions can be taken by reading it. Quantum mechanics at present yields a coherent structure of *mathematics*. However, its *physical concepts* resemble the giving of directions to find one's way through a city.[75]

Reaction within the physics community to the critics of quantum theory has been resolute. A Nobel physicist at Berkeley says:

> Present quantum theory can explain everything that the hidden variable theory can. Moreover, we are all thoroughly familiar with the instrumental apparatus of quantum research and our measurements have a high degree of precision. Now why should we want to scrap all of this for some philosophical principle that is supposed to restore causality?

His colleagues were equally insistent. According to one:

> Although Bohm and company are respected physicists, their opposition to quantum theory is very philosophical. Hidden variables may exist, but so far none has been detected and until they are, I will remain unperturbed. One must have solid, perhaps even massive evidence before quantum theory can be successfully challenged.

[75] Bohm and Bub, "A Proposed Solution," pp. 457–458.

A Purdue physicist put the matter even more bluntly.

> Most of the people currently advocating a deterministic physics are older men — men who were raised on the classical physics and never accepted the quantum theory. In my judgment there is really no new evidence to support a deterministic theory. Its advocates are merely victims of wishful thinking.

At the University of Texas (Austin) a particle physicist expressed himself this way:

> The kind of conflict created by Bohm, de Broglie, and Margenau is not something you teach to students. It lies on the periphery of research. It is quite tentative, quite exploratory. I think I am right in suggesting that most physicists are too pragmatic to be drawn to the problem. Perhaps an analogy will illustrate what I mean: most physicists are about as much concerned with hidden variables as they are with modern art.

Throughout the interviews a pattern tended to emerge which may indicate why it is so difficult to displace an established theory. Physicists willingly admit that any number of novel theories may be formulated to challenge the basic assumptions of a theory in use. However, while not harmful in itself, a preoccupation with theory construction can mean not only a loss of focus, but a waste of time for a practicing scientist. Consequently, only new theories proposed by respected members of the profession are likely to receive attention; even then, measurable results must be produced *in sufficient quantity* to demonstrate that the new theory can explain phenomena significantly better than an alteration in existing theory.

SCIENCE AND THE PROBLEM OF LEGITIMACY

The general attitude of the physics community toward the hidden-variable theory is that it is neither useful nor interesting; as a result, little research has been sponsored in its behalf.[76] To outsiders this response may appear unnecessary and

---

[76] See Fred J. Belinfante, "Experiments to Disprove that Nature Would be Deterministic," unpublished symposium paper, Purdue University, 1970. The latest "general" account of the conflict is "Quantum Mechanics Debate," *Physics Today* 24, no. 4 (April 1971): 36–44.

unscientific.[77] For on the face of it, subquantum theory is both
plausible and appealing. Physicists, however, are rarely prepared
to endorse a theory that undermines the normal routines of observation and research — unless, of course, the prevailing theory
encounters difficulties that cannot be explained by ad hoc solutions. Yet the crucial question is: By what mechanism or process
does a scientist realize that change or resistance is in order? How
does he know when it is appropriate to mend the current theory
or to strike out along bold new lines? [78] If the results of this study
are meaningful, the answer lies in the political techniques used by
the profession to ensure the perceptual reliability of its work.
Through such "instruments" as persuasion, argument, ridicule,
and coercion, disciplinary activity is channeled into the productive "energy" of significant research. In this sense "politics" not
only enables science to protect and expand its epistemic investment, but it helps the entire enterprise extend its perceptual
"grip" into areas showing a high probability of reward.

   To explain the operation of science in these terms is to under-
mine the popular image of what constitutes legitimate research.
Most people are taught to believe that science is a democratic
form of inquiry — a form characterized by the absence of prejudice, tradition, and overhead authority. Accordingly, if science
is all it claims to be, any theory should be met with critical discussion, not with professional apathy or contempt. To laymen
who have maintained this belief the discovery that professionalized science is neither democratic nor antiseptic must come as a
disillusionment. This also matters to established scientists who
realize the extent to which acceptable theories depend upon institutional certification. As John Ziman confesses:

   It is quite evident . . . that certification as a competent scientist
   is entirely in the hands of the existing Establishment. The teach-

[77] For example, Mario Bunge, an old opponent of quantum theory, has put
the matter strongly: "For the first time in history, scientists have managed
to out-dogmatize philosophers." Quoted in Bernhard, "Skeleton in the
Closet," p. 30.

[78] The political problems inherent in this question are strikingly similar to
those posed by Burke and Paine.

ers, examiners and referees are all "authorities" — well meaning no doubt, but incapable of treating a genuine unorthodoxy — a reversion, say, to Lamarckism, or non-relativistic physics, or deterministic electron theory — as better than a mental aberration. This closure, this ecclesiastical tendency, of modern Science is nothing to be shrugged off lightly. It does conflict with the ideal of the freely accepted consensus, and threatens the basis of its credibility.[79]

Ziman's pungent remarks open the way for further reflection on the legitimacy of professionalized science. Together with the controversies already discussed they pose an interesting question: How does science justify itself to society in view of its elitist structure and its internal techniques of control? The traditional defense was to deny altogether that antidemocratic tendencies exist; but with the increasing pressure to make scientific resources available to the larger social system, a new rationale is emerging. It has been present, in one form or another, since science first requested public support, but its contemporary expression is much more direct and systematic. The new justification for scientific research is based on the concept of utility and is increasingly responsive to the needs and priorities of the nation state.

The Democratic Defense. The traditional defense of professionalized science is a variation on two closely related themes: first, the science is a completely free and open system of inquiry — one that structurally resembles democracy; and second, its efforts are solely directed toward the discovery and communication of new truths. It is almost impossible to find prominent scientists who do not acknowledge the legitimacy of these goals or who refuse to affirm that both are achieved within the social system of science. J. Robert Oppenheimer, for example, has categorically stated that within all scientific disciplines, "there is no one to blame if the picture does not make sense." [80] The positive virtues acquired from scientific work, he notes, are to be found in the ideal of

---

[79] Ziman, *Public Knowledge*, p. 65.

[80] J. Robert Oppenheimer, *The Open Mind* (New York: Simon and Schuster, 1955), p. 96.

"open-mindedness," for "the scientist is free to ask any question, . . . to seek for any evidence, to correct any error." [81] Marcus Goodall of M.I.T. has put the matter even more succinctly: "Science is a genuinely democratic enterprise where the individual can be heard, and which has largely built-in guarantees that it is not going to get spoilt." [82]

The implicit assumption behind the democratic defense of science is that no one possesses absolute and final knowledge. Given this premise, the only political system appropriate to scientific research is one emphasizing an impulse to change. To its defenders this means that only under democratic conditions can science achieve its full potential — both in its internal operations and in its external relations with larger society. One of the most striking examples of philosophical support for this justification is rooted in an essay by Charles Sanders Pierce called "The Scientific Attitude and Fallibilism." Throughout the work Pierce contends that since no one (including scientists) can be absolutely certain about empirical observations, the only reasonable attitude is: "Do not block the way of inquiry." [83] Following Pierce, Thomas Landon Thorson urges that this "ultimate 'must' of science" can be translated into the only reasonable maxim for justifying democracy: "Do not block the possibility of change with respect to social goals." [84] Although these arguments are ideological defenses of the "internal" similarities between science and democracy, others exist that affirm the interdependency of science and democratic institutions. Robert Merton is perhaps the best example here. He maintains that "science is afforded opportunity for development in a democratic order which is integrated with the ethos of science." [85] While recognizing that "the most diverse social structures have provided some measure of support to science," he is

[81] *Ibid.*, p. 114.

[82] Marcus C. Goodall, *Science and the Politician* (Cambridge, Mass.: Schenkman Publishing Company, 1965), p. 62.

[83] Justus Buchler, ed., *The Philosophical Writing of Pierce: Selected Writings* (London: Routledge and Kegan Paul, 1940), p. 54. See also p. 59.

[84] Thomas L. Thorson, *The Logic of Democracy* (New York: Holt, Rinehart & Winston, 1962), pp. 121, 139.

[85] Robert K. Merton, *Social Theory and Social Structure* (New York: The Free Press, 1957), p. 552.

convinced that the fullest measure of development is produced in a democratic institutional context.[86]

The democratic defense of science is surely its most popular and fashionable bulwark. It occupies an important place in the philosophical works of Mead and Dewey; [87] and as the popular sympathy for Velikovsky illustrates, it has now become a part of the conventional expectation of scientific practice. But there are signs within the scientific community that this justification may prove ineffective against empirical appraisals of scientific work. It appears that the strongest current of opposition is represented by those who believe that science can justify itself on the basis of utility and technical achievement alone. But scientists like Michael Polanyi are not altogether convinced. While they reject the democratic defense, they are mindful of Polanyi's warning.

> To defend science against lay rebellions on the grounds of its technical achievements may be precarious. To pretend that science is open-minded, when it is not, may prove equally perilous. But to declare that the ultimate purpose of science is to understand nature may seem old fashioned and ineffectual. And to confess further how greatly such explanations of nature rely on vague and undemonstrable conceptions of reality may sound positively scandalous. But since all of this is in fact true, might it not prove safest to say so? [88]

The Utility Defense. Polanyi's concern is well taken, for powerful external forces are already redefining the function of science. The autonomous posture characterizing science since its emergence is under attack; the reasons are not that science is an ideological threat to the nation state or that its operations are dangerous to the power structures of society. Rather, science is gradually being forced from its autonomous role because its knowledge together with its skills and techniques are essential to institutional

---

[86] *Ibid.*

[87] See George H. Mead, *The Philosophy of the Act* (Chicago: University of Chicago Press, 1938), pp. 662–663; and John Dewey, "Creative Democracy — The Task Before Us" in *The Philosopher and the Common Man: Essays in Honor of John Dewey to Celebrate His Eightieth Birthday* (New York: Greenwood Press, 1968), p. 228.

[88] Polanyi, "The Growth of Science in Society," p. 541.

growth. Charles Merriam anticipated this tendency long before it became recognized as a significant social problem. In 1934 he wrote:

> With the vast growth of science and the immense projection of the school and of research, it may be said that science is accorded a seat at the table of power, almost, although not quite perhaps, recognized as one of the family. . . . [But] science is not ambitious for autonomous government or group independence as are many of the other members of the family, and in that sense does not threaten the position of the political power. . . . The other members of the family of power look a little askance at science. [But] they rejoice in its powerful aid in propaganda, in war, in industry, in its support of the various claims advanced by different groups from time to time.[89]

These remarks are all the more telling when placed within the context of Clark Kerr's recent analysis of the American university. The autonomous system has been able to survive largely because the institutional role of the university shielded it from external influences. But as Kerr points out, the university is now under pressure "to respond to the expanding claims of national service; to merge its activities with industry as never before; to adapt to and rechannel new intellectual currents."[90] In short, the university is becoming a service institution for the activities of larger society. The importance of this new role is rationalized by showing its functional utility for sustaining the institutions of an expanding economy, for providing military research and defense, and for underwriting a postwelfare state. Kerr does not, however, shirk from these prospects; he fully embraces them as a paradigm for worldwide imitation. "By the end of this period," he concludes, "there will be a truly American university, an institution not looking to other models but serving itself, as a model for universities in other parts of the globe."[91]

[89] Charles Merriam, *Political Power* (New York: McGraw-Hill, 1934), pp. 81–82.

[90] Clark Kerr, *The Uses of the University* (Cambridge, Mass.: Harvard University Press, 1963), p. 86.

[91] *Ibid.*

Table 4.7 Popular Support for Science

Question	Number	Strongly Agree	Agree	Can't Say	Disagree	Strongly Disagree	Total
26[a]	838	22.3%	66.4%	5.3%	5.4%	.3%	99.7%

[a] Question 26: "Most people do not understand what science is about but they accept its authority because they can see its frequent demonstration of power (bombs, rockets to the moon, new medical techniques, etc.)."

As the university becomes structurally integrated into the power conglomerates of society, science is left to the mercy of benefactors with other motives than the understanding of nature. According to J. D. Bernal, science

> has now become something very different from that which started with the academies of the seventeenth century, though these remain as honorific bodies. Its purpose has changed and its scale has become enormously greater. Its concern is with the use of science both . . . in the evolution of the economy and administration of states whose major technical interest has become the preparation of war.[92]

Most scientists are not as outspoken as Bernal, but the results of the survey questionnaire show their keen awareness of where popular support for science lies. It does not rest in the aesthetic wonder of probing nature's secrets, but in a visible display of power — such as the development of nuclear weaponry and delivery vehicles, the construction of lunar transport systems, the discovery and proliferation of new medical techniques. (See Table 4.7.)

The pervasive utility of science to the power structures of society is gradually eroding the old industrial ideologies that took as their model of reality either capitalism or socialism. The new ideology depends upon technocratic elites aligned with political, military, and industrial organizations. Lakoff, in fact, feels that this development portends the emergence of a "scientific society"

[92] J. D. Bernal, *Science in History* (New York: Hawthorn Books, 1965), p. 929.

where "elites . . . function as a surrogate for an absent and incompetent democracy." From such a perspective it is not surprising that he insists, "Decision making in scientific society . . . works through a combination of professional elitism and limited democracy, with the result that the system is really one of managerial democracy." [93] The ideology emerging for this unprecedented set of relations carries with it a strong, if not a preponderant, emphasis upon economy of effort and efficiency of resource allocation. In analyzing its content Lakoff calls the new ideology "systems analysis" and defines it as

> an effort to apply the scientific method, roughly and artfully, to all areas of policy-making. The method arose in wartime operations research — another indication of the critical transitional role played by the effort to use science and technology for military purposes — and has been developed into the basis for much of modern military planning. In recent years it has been proposed, chiefly by civilians who introduced the method in the defense sector, that this mode of analysis be adapted to non-military objectives in such sensitive areas as health and welfare, crime, poverty, transportation, and housing. In short, what . . . began as an effort to get help from scientists, engineers, and economists in technical matters where military expertise was not considered sufficient, has now developed into a broad effort to make all decision making as scientific as possible.[94]

Although Lakoff does not provide a detailed explanation of what is involved, systems analysis constitutes a statistical estimate of probable utility. It is suited to a decision-making environment in which objectives are clearly specified and ways to cut costs can be evaluated through mathematical techniques. As Wildavsky says:

> The systems analyst first decides what questions are relevant to his inquiry, selects certain quantifiable factors, cuts down the list of factors to be dealt with by aggregation and by eliminating the (hopefully) less important ones, and then gives them quantitative

[93] Sanford Lakoff, "Scientific Society: Notes toward a Paradigm," in Paul J. Piccard, ed., *Science and Policy Issues* (Itasca, Ill.: Peacock Publishers, 1969), p. 65.
[94] *Ibid.*, p. 66.

relationships with one another within the system he has chosen for analysis.[95]

These techniques are a response to institutional developments that try to replace the amorphous boundaries of uncertainty with decisional estimates of probable risk. The more complex the environment within which institutional decisions must be made, the greater the chances that utility methods will be employed as a justification for rational coordination and control.

Professionalized science, of course, is not fully "rationalized," but its pattern of elitist politics bears a curious resemblance to the decisional processes of larger institutional structures. Moreover, given the "external" pressure to orient its research toward items of national priority (such as defense, health, conservation, transportation, etc.), the autonomous system finds it increasingly difficult to resort to adaptive methods of decision-making. They are simply too cumbersome and inefficient. Thus, as science becomes more institutionalized, even areas of research not directly applicable to national missions are apt to undergo transformation.

The historical style of decision-making in science — the one emphasizing criticism, controversy, and spontaneous consensus — may be replaced by one stressing conflict, competition, and manipulated consensus. The emergence of this style is perhaps a direct result of an institutional attempt to economize cognitive and physical resources.

Yet the older justification of science and its style of operation dies hard. In an interview with a physicist from the Lincoln Laboratory, I was shown a letter he had recently received from a Latin American scientist. As an outsider, the Latin American was concerned with what he thought was a lack of significant theoretical debate among professional physicists in the United States. The American scientist was perhaps sensitive to this charge, but his response is worth noting. "Physics could never get anywhere if we debated things in this way. And yet, it is surprising how many people still believe we can." The criticism of the Latin American, however, is typical of the "democratic" expectation of scientific performance. In this sense, its major points merit attention.

> I think I know how to correct . . . this untenable situation [the present state of physics]: the old way of discussing and debating things has to be re-introduced at the universities, research institutes, and scientific societies. When I say "to debate" I do not mean just a *polite* exchange of words among people who were educated the same way and consequently think basically the same way.
>
> I mean to create "competitive debates" the type which, for instance, occurred between the scholastics and Galileo.
>
> I mean "debates" where the "principles" used by one group are challenged by the other. . . .
>
> And do we try such unorthodox ways today? You know very well that all universities and all research institutes will perform only the experiments their professional physicists will propose and in a way they see them to be made — no opposition is involved or even thought of. Don't you find this funny in a country where in politics for instance there is a free opposition, the voice of which is, at least, heard if not many times followed?

Even though the advanced empirical disciplines have moved far beyond the conflict patterns inherent in "democratic debate," the older expectations still persist.

The Problem of Control. The growing institutionalization of science and its utility rationale raise questions concerning its ultimate control. The democratic defense of science does not have to anticipate problems of this order, for control is considered a function of democratic participation. Even Polanyi, who denies the democratic organization of science, feels compelled to argue for a system of autonomous management. Instead of each scientist standing watch over all his colleagues, Polanyi suggests that the autonomous system can be effectively checked by "judgments extending over *neighborhoods* [scientific specialties, that] . . . overlap and form a chain spanning the entire range of sciences." [96]

---

[96] Polanyi, "The Growth of Science in Society," p. 543, emphasis mine.

The increasing emphasis upon science as an essential instrument of national wealth and power has brought Polanyi's argument under serious review. Beneath the banner that "science is too important to be left to scientists," new attempts are being made to rethink the problem of autonomous regulation. As these proposals emerge, so does their basic premise that professionalized science may become an integral part of the power institutions of larger society.

5

Conclusion: the future of professionalized science

THE ENTANGLING RELATIONS between the scientific community and governmental, military, and economic institutions are likely to become even more complex in the future. The prospect of a cybernated and research-oriented economy, international competition, and the dependence of military power upon techno-scientific advances demand the planned use of science as a national priority. What is often missed in assessing these developments, however, is an awareness of the extent to which science has always seemed dependent upon other institutions — not only for material support, but for models of organization as well.

Defenders of the autonomous system compare it, not coincidentally, to the conditions of economic laissez-faire. In its early stages of organization, professionalized science resembled in some ways a nascent capitalistic economy — complete with an ethic of individualism and an emphasis on the unrestricted communication of ideas (a doctrine with obvious similarities to free trade). Moreover, during the first part of the nineteenth century when scientific research had no permanent institutional moorings, many of its leaders questioned whether the enterprise could survive. Despite the inclusion of scientific subjects in university curricula later in the century, science was not assured economic viability until its skills were of some use to government and industry.

Although the initial connections between science and society were tenuous and circumspect, that is no longer the case. The corporate revolution, together with the breakdown of an effective distinction between public and private enterprise,[1] has drastically multiplied the organizational settings within which scientific research occurs. As these conditions become more sharply focused, the model of science as an autonomous activity becomes increasingly problematic. In the revealing candor of Norman Storer:

> I am suggesting that the new position of science in society has engendered internal conditions which are rapidly altering its entire structure. The two sources of change — increased support from outside and increasing growth inside — are operating to open wide the older, closed-system scientific community which we may still be assuming or hoping will be preserved. I suggest that it will *not* be preserved, and that we must accept this and bend our efforts toward preserving what we can of it in the new situation which is nearly upon us.[2]

In short, the autonomous system, with its stress upon "entrepreneurial" research, no longer seems an adequate description of the far-flung activities of science. As Merton notes, the old and familiar parameters of science are being stretched to exaggerated dimensions:

> The social organization of scientific inquiry has greatly changed, with collaboration and research teams the order of the day. As just another pale reflection of this changed organization of scientific inquiry, each decade registers more and more multi-authored articles in decided contrast to the almost unchanging

[1] Sanford A. Lakoff, "Scientific Society: Notes toward a Paradigm" in Paul J. Piccard, ed., *Science and Policy Issues* (Itasca, Ill.: Peacock Publishers, 1969), p. 57.

[2] Quoted in Warren O. Hagstrom, *The Scientific Community* (New York: Basic Books, 1965), p. 295.

character of single-authored papers in the humanities. . . . The vast increase in numbers of scientists and in funds for science practically dictates the exponential increase in the quantity of published research. As science has become more institutionalized, it has also become more intimately interrelated with the other institutions of society. Science-based technologies and the partial diffusion of a scientific outlook have become great social forces that move our history and greatly affect the relations obtaining between the nations of the world.[3]

The expansion of professionalized science into so many diverse areas may be attributed in large measure to the availability of funds from government and industry. But the impact of this development upon the theoretical structure of science has been to fragment research into increasingly abstract and isolated compartments. Today, the greatest internal problem facing science is how to preserve the focus and reliability of its work in an atmosphere of proliferating specialization and semantic confusion (Chapter 3).

Science has responded to the crisis by integrating and reintegrating its research at successively higher levels of abstraction. In following this strategy, its methodological values may have experienced a significant displacement. To argue that the methods of science are directed toward revealing nature's truths is now considered old-fashioned. Nature has simply lost its meaning as a concrete category; it has become institutionalized — stamped by the minute division of its former estate into thousands of tiny research provinces. The goal of science emerging from this context is *not* one of simple observation and discovery, but rather one where institutional certification becomes the ultimate ideal of perceptual reliability and the gateway to scientific knowledge.[4]

Both the ideal and practice of certification is an institutional response to a highly abstract level of scientific achievement. The problems and experiments of contemporary science are no longer

---

[3] Robert K. Merton, "Behavior Patterns of Scientists," *The American Scholar* 38, no. 2 (Spring 1969): 200.

[4] See Robert K. Merton's discussion of the institutional value of science in his *Social Theory and Social Structure* (Glencoe, Ill.: The Free Press, 1949), p. 309.

the "classic" ones of watching apples fall from trees, or rolling balls down inclined planes. As Weinberg has shown (Chapter 3), professionalized science is confronted with higher order abstractions that subsume previous levels of "concrete" work. (For example, quantum mechanics accounts for the Balmer series in hydrogen, topology integrates some aspects of nonlinear differential equations, and the Watson-Crick model brings together a number of biological achievements.) Precisely these conditions allow politics to play such a vital role in the perceptive capacity of professionalized science. In place of the concrete experience of nature, scientists are forced to rely upon consensual models (abstractions) of an external world that has become largely artificial. To maintain the reliability of their perceptions, they subject conflicting interpretations to political processes which ultimately screen out those that seem suspect and direct attention to those that can maximize the research yield of accepted paradigms.

Under these conditions, the scope and intensity of political conflicts within the empirical sciences may well depend upon the "regime conditions" prevailing in each discipline and the relative position of elite groups inside them (Chapter 5). Regime conditions in turn respond to the level of theoretical development that each discipline has achieved. In the tightly integrated disciplines of physics, astronomy, and chemistry, for example, regime conditions are likely to be oligarchic and elite relations characterized by interlocking postures. In biology and geology, regime conditions appear to be differently structured. On balance, they are defined by conditions of competitive pluralism, with the position of decisional elites in proximate relation to each other. Finally, disputes within the well-developed disciplines are, under normal circumstances, shorter and much narrower in scope than those in more loosely defined fields of research. The available evidence suggests that this is due to two factors: first, fewer active participants are involved; and second, the matters in dispute grow out of interests in the precision of concept specification (that is, refining the measurable parameters of a concept), rather than concern over the validity of the concept itself.

As long as scientific disputes are confined to the autonomous system, there seems little chance that they will provoke widespread public attention, since the debates are almost always too abstract and technical for nonscientists to grasp. But the prospective thrust of science is outward, beyond the autonomous confines. Here, its knowledge and skill are increasingly subject to cooptation and use by power institutions seeking to gain more influence by creating additional resources. Without conscious intent, but offering little resistance, professionalized science seems to have advanced as a nationalized activity. Unlike controversies within the autonomous system, this development is likely to have a pervasive effect upon public awareness, for the issue it raises concerns the evolving relations between science and the balances of power within the larger political system.

POLITICAL POWER AND THE SPATIAL DIMENSIONS OF SCIENCE

Perhaps in the last analysis the spatial possibilities open to science may greatly depend upon how its activities are affected by power configurations within society as a whole. Thus, while the internal politics of science serves to refine and focus scientific perceptions, the external politics of power may ultimately define the institutional arrangements under which scientific work is established. This point is essential to an understanding of the future dimensions of science, for it suggests that the organization of political power can create the spatial opportunities or "fields of vision" structuring the scientific enterprise.

Both analytically and historically the direction that science has assumed in the United States appears intimately linked to the emergence of three distinct but overlapping systems of political power. Although intricate and complicated in operation, these configurations may be roughly characterized as the liberal state, the bureaucratic state, and the postindustrial state. Somewhat unconventionally, I will suggest that the traditional practices of science as well as its future possibilities may depend largely upon the organizational constraints that each system of power imposes. While this perspective is necessarily broad, it may prove useful in understanding the diverse activities of contemporary science and the nature of its involvement with the major complexes of political decision-making. Moreover, by viewing the spatial characteristics of science as a response to changing patterns of institutional power, an important step has been taken toward identifying a part of the generic influences active in shaping the perceptual scope of scientific work.

Still, several difficulties must be mentioned. The configurations of power are not mutually exclusive; each intrudes upon the others and all three operate simultaneously. The essential analytical task is not to deny that weaker institutional forms exist, but to determine under what circumstances one set of power arrangements appears dominant and others recessive. Although this undertaking may lack a degree of theoretical elegance, it nevertheless represents an appreciation of the accretional nature of modern society and the persistence of institutional patterns. In terms of the present study precisely this awareness serves as a framework for relating simple models of scientific activity (such as those developed in Chapter 2) to larger systems of political reality.

Professionalized Science and the Liberal State. The emergence of distinct professional characteristics in science owes an enormous debt to the existence of a central political organization with rather limited interests in the promotion and development of scientific knowledge. Although Hunter Dupree has forcefully argued to the contrary, his analysis does not sufficiently distinguish between on the one hand, science as a body of theoretical knowledge and, on the other, selected technologies utilized by the federal government in geographical exploration, maritime surveys, and military procurement. Succinctly, Dupree's position is this:

> From the beginning the [national] government proved able and willing to use the science of the day not only for its own internal needs but as a boon to its citizens. The Lewis and Clark expedition and the Coast Survey were early examples of what became after 1830 the systematic use of science in all phases of exploration, both of the westward reaches of the continent and of the sea lanes that carried American commerce around the world. During the Civil War, glimpses of other uses of science widened its scope, and in the two generations following 1865 a great scientific establishment arose within the government, developing its own typical organization around the problems it faced, recruiting

a specialized personnel, and contributing greatly to the scientific resources of the country.[5]

Dupree's perspective, however, takes little, if any, notice of the rise of scientific disciplines, the establishment of scholarly journals, and the creation of professional standards of research. This omission should not be taken to mean that these activities were peripheral to the development of science. Indeed, without them the structure of scientific knowledge would have suffered greatly and its growth retarded decisively. As will be shown, practices essential to the professionalization of science did not derive from governmental sponsorship, but grew out of the peculiar relationship between the liberal (or constitutional) state and a social realm of "private," internalized controls.

In theory, the concentration of power within the liberal state was narrowly defined and intricately circumscribed by an institutional field of countervailing forces. In the United States these restrictive features found expression in a doctrine of separation of powers, checks and balances, and federalism. The purpose behind these restraints went beyond the foundations of a "balanced government" with limited powers. At bottom, the liberal dream was to create two distinct systems of regulation — one public, the other private; one synoptic in operation and the other governed by patterns of mutual adjustment. The public realm was conceived as small and uniform; the private as large and diverse. Part of what this distinction came to mean is rendered by John Schaar's analysis of constitutional theory:

> The [liberal] state specified that all men shall, within a prescribed area, behave in the same way. It then defines or constitutes this area in which behavior must be uniform as the public realm: the public realm *is* the area of uniform and equal behavior. This space is kept as small as possible, so that the private space can be as large as possible. Liberty, which expresses men's inequalities . . . resides within the zone of privacy. . . . the sharp distinction between public and private, and the subordination of the former to the latter, narrows the stage of public action. When the public

[5] A. Hunter Dupree, *Science in the Federal Government* (Cambridge, Mass.: Harvard University Press, 1957), pp. 375–376.

space is so circumscribed, the perils of contingent action are surely reduced — this was a major aim of the constitutionalists — but so too are the possibilities.[6]

It should not be inferred from Schaar's account that the "zone of privacy" was one where restraints upon individual behavior were absent. The emergence of the liberal state did not mean an abandonment of the private sphere to individual impulse and initiative. Rather, by reducing the synoptic activities of the central government, the liberal state made possible an alternative system of control that used a completely different set of "regulatory principles." Instead of the traditional methods of force and coercion, management in the private sphere could rely upon various social, psychological, and economic sanctions to discourage unwanted behavior. Wolin describes this system clearly:

> Liberalism has always been accused of seeking to dissolve the solidarities of social ties and relationships and to replace them by the unfettered, independent individual, the masterless man. In reality, the charge is almost without foundation and completely misses the liberal addiction towards social conformity. . . . [Social conformity] implies, first, that the individual "adjust" his tastes, actions, and style of life to a social denominator. . . . Secondly, social conformity not only assumes that individual adaptation will contribute to social cohesion and order, but that a happy and successful life for the individual can be attained only by observing society's standards; that is, the generalized expression of the wants, values, and expectations held by most of the members. Thirdly, and most crucially, the individual is invited to do more than "accept" social norms; their external quality must be overcome so that they can be appropriated into the inner life of the individual. In short, social norms should be internalized and, as such, operate as the individual's conscience.[7]

[6] John Schaar, "Some Ways of Thinking about Equality," *Journal of Politics* 26 (November 1964): 886, 888. See also M. J. C. Vile, *Constitutionalism and the Separation of Powers* (Oxford: Clarendon Press, 1967); and Kirk Thompson, "Constitutional Theory and Political Action," *Journal of Politics*, Vol. 31 (August 1969).

[7] Sheldon S. Wolin, *Politics and Vision* (Boston: Little, Brown, 1960), p. 343.

Internalizing social norms, however, was not spontaneous. More than anything else, success was a tribute to the manipulation of threats and inducements beyond the province of the state. In discussing Locke's contribution to this body of thought, Wolin again provides an interpretation of its operation:

> [Locke] touched on two basic themes which became central in later liberal theories. In the first place, he clearly indicated that social norms could be understood as a species of control distinct from political power or legal authority. Secondly, Locke posed for the individual conscience the problem of social definitions of ethical values: . . . If the individual were compelled to confront society's norms as equal in status to ethical choices of any type, the consequences of non-conformity would be more serious. For the heavy sanctions which society could bring to bear — economic, social, and psychological — rendered an act of defiance far more consequential than any action of a private variety.[8]

The issue that Locke posed dealt with a configuration of power that permitted the emergence of a "private" system of control sustained by patterns of mutual adjustment. This was thought desirable, since the state was not regarded as a source of either actual or potential creativity. Moreover, the norms upon which the private system was based were drawn from the community at large, and were "enforced" by social, psychological, and economic pressures. Both the recognition of nonlegal norms and the informal patterns of "enforcement" constituted the regulatory mechanism of the private sphere.

Even though Locke's defense of liberal society was not drawn from a thorough review of historical evidence, the emergence of professionalized science in the United States was closely patterned after its prescriptions. It is true that many scientists complained bitterly of poverty and destitution, but the relationship between science and government was nevertheless kept relatively autonomous until the latter part of the nineteenth century. As Van Tassel and Hall have observed, "During the whole span from the close of the Revolution through 1865, neither the economy nor the political structure of the country was conducive to any continuous or large scale public support of scientific or other

---

[8] *Ibid.*, pp. 343–344.

cultural institutions." [9] An important consequence of this condition was the creation of a system of internal controls that resembled the Lockean emphasis on social norms and "private" sanctions. While perhaps this mode of adjustment may now seem overshadowed by external features of regulation, it continues to serve as the behavioral paradigm of professionalized science. In Hagstrom's widely accepted formulation,

> the autonomy of the scientific community cannot be taken for granted; it must be maintained by internal social controls, among other things. [Moreover] . . . commitments to norms tend to erode in the absence of reinforcement. . . . In the absence of sanctions, deviance from such norms would be common. We may conclude that the socialization of scientists must be supplemented by a dynamic system of social control, if the values and effectiveness of science are to be maintained.[10]

The effect of an autonomous system of regulation upon the theoretical pursuits of science should not be underestimated. The kind of research problems associated with professionalized science are heavily dependent upon internal sanctions and rewards. In fact, Hagstrom has suggested:

> Basic science is unlike other professions in that its practitioners not only claim autonomy in determining procedures to be used in the course of the work and in evaluating the success of these procedures; they also claim the right to decide for themselves the problems they should select and, on the basis of their work and that of others, whether or not theories are true. . . . Problems are not "given" to basic scientists by others or by "nature," at least in the most important instances. Rather problems are discovered and invented by scientists.[11]

Although it is important to recognize that scientists are actively engaged in shaping their "realities," Hagstrom's account does not explicitly describe the tactics of pressure and manipulation (i.e., the politics) responsible for certain methodologies and research problems in science. Yet precisely this aspect of control

---

[9] David D. Van Tassel and Michael G. Hall, *Science and Society in the United States* (Homewood, Ill.: The Dorsey Press, 1966), p. 23.

[10] Hagstrom, *The Scientific Community*, p. 12.

[11] *Ibid.*, pp. 108–109.

constitutes the regulatory mechanism of the autonomous system.

Related to this is another point that should be stressed: the extent to which the internal politics of science can operate depends upon its spatial proximity to the central political organization. If that relation is distant, the scope of professionalized science will be determined by its own forces of manipulation and adjustment. If not, external political influences will begin to intrude, and science may find it necessary to adjust its traditional practices to accommodate new demands. The relatively autonomous posture that professionalized science assumed toward the federal government during its formative years finally did give way under the pressures of the twentieth century. But its essential expectations have lingered. In fact, as this study reveals (Chapter 3), the larger part of the professional community of science has not relinquished its claim to an autonomous relation with the power institutions of society. Although the autonomous system considers it proper to solicit grants from government and industry, the system also encourages the belief that contributions should be made in the spirit of a disinterested patron whose only return is the discovery of new knowledge.

The Bureaucratic State. As Allen Schick has convincingly argued, the configuration of power that characterized the liberal state began to change with "the growth of national industry, the creation of new regulatory instruments and agencies prompted by that growth and the mobilization of administrative expertise to manage public activities." [12] These developments represented the first stage of the transition to the bureaucratic state and covered roughly the period from the creation of the Interstate Commerce Commission (1887) to the New Deal. The second stage, which began with the Roosevelt administration, added to the existing routines of administrative regulation the expansion of departmental and agency missions and the powerful thrust of public ownership itself. As Schick has described it:

> Though the federal government had assumed a *doing* role in selected programs many years earlier, the New Deal era can be re-

[12] Allen Schick, "The Cybernetic State," *Transaction* 7, no. 4 (February 1970): 15.

garded as the great leap to bureaucratics. The bureaucratic state was designed to replace the market with public enterprises, not merely to correct for its deficiencies. . . . In the bureaucratic state, the administrative and political are joined, united by interest-group brokers who traffic between the bureaucracies and the people and weave complex clientele-congressional bureau relationships for the purpose of channeling the public enterprises into the service of private interests. A new public market thus is created, resembling the private one in certain aspects, but lacking both the ultimate test of profit and the unremitting competition of adversaries. Interests bargain with one another at the public trough, but they also form coalitions and drive out competition when it suits their objectives.[13]

The power realities behind the bureaucratic state are mirrored in the complex interactions that link different centers of governmental decision-making to private clienteles and interest groups. Unlike the liberal state in which governmental power was confined to a rather limited sphere of operation, the bureaucratic state represents a marked expansion of state activities in the area of economic regulation and governmental service. Thus the role of government is enlarged, but its capacity to act depends upon its ability to build supporting coalitions (both public and private) at all levels of decision-making.

The impact of such a dispersed power structure upon professionalized science has been, first of all, to establish a new framework for allocating scientific resources and, second, to exploit conflicts within the scientific community concerning matters of national policy. The most immediate and pervasive effect of the bureaucratic state has been the increased number of institutions that play an instrumental role in shaping the politics of research allocations. As Daniel Greenberg suggests:

The laissez-faire system [i.e., professionalized science] takes place within the bounds of an intricately constructed, subtly functioning system of government that, in effect, defines the possibilities of science by governing the availability and use of resources. If the system is not bound by rigid policy, it is nonetheless bound by well-rooted practice and custom. If its principal political ob-

---

[13] *Ibid.*, pp. 16–17. I have treated Schick's concept of the administrative state as the first stage of the bureaucratic state.

jective is the maintenance of independence, it is an objective that is pursued within the limitations imposed by the various authorities that provide funds.[14]

But the bureaucratic state does more to science than limit its research activity by controlling levels of funding. Its political structure is effectively designed to take advantage of disagreements within the scientific community relating not only to the overall purposes of government, but to specific policy positions as well. Since political success within the bureaucratic state depends upon the careful construction of public-private coalitions, scientific judgment is frequently enlisted to defend interests that are diametrically opposed. In fact, it is common to see scientists vehemently divided over such issues as environmental pollution, the feasibility of weapons systems, and the possibility of arms control. To some extent this feature of the bureaucratic state has been mildly countered by attempts within a few scientific disciplines to encourage their journals, as well as their associations, to take corporate positions on matters of national controversy. Although details of several struggles of this nature will appear later, it is necessary, in order to place them in proper perspective, to focus briefly upon the intricate mechanism through which the bureaucratic state tries to manage its scientific investment.

To relate precisely how the bureaucratic state controls and coordinates its allocations to science is difficult, for the process involves multiple overlays of public and private decision-making that tax one's capacity to invent and refine descriptive categories. Historically, of course, the relationship between professionalized science and the bureaucratic state developed slowly — at least until the outbreak of the Second World War. The events of war, however, accelerated tendencies already present in the private sphere (especially in industry) and created organizational ties between science and government that were to become the foundation of a much closer relation. As Greenberg notes:

> The war demonstrated not only that big organization, big equipment, and generous funding were compatible with the creative

[14] Daniel S. Greenberg, *The Politics of Pure Science* (New York: The New American Library, 1967), p. 152.

process, but that with war-born instruments and technology ready to be applied to basic research, bigness had become indispensable in many fields of research, especially physics.[15]

For the professional scientific community the most important consequence of the war was the creation of a new system of institutional supervision and control. After a thorough review of its characteristics, the National Academy of Sciences elected to call the new order an "interrelated system," [16] for the term described the network of relations that had evolved from the wartime alliance among university scientists, industry, and the federal government. Recently Robert Gilpin has furnished a much more elaborate description.

The first feature of the interrelated system is that important aspects of decision making for science have shifted from universities and private institutions and become highly centralized in several governmental agencies. This is due to the increasing need of scientists for substantial financial support by the government. Though the initiation of research projects rests largely with individual researchers and research institutions, the decisions concerning which projects are to be supported, and to what extent, are now made to a considerable extent by such agencies as the National Science Foundation, the National Institutes of Health, the Defense Department, and the Atomic Energy Commission. With respect to basic research, however, these decisions are made largely on the advice of scientific advisors to these agencies.

. . . The second feature . . . of the . . . interrelated system is the use by the national government of the research contract (or project grant in the case of basic research) as a primary instrument for financing the national research and development effort. Research teams, universities, and industries are not administratively subordinate to the agencies of government supporting research; this gives both government and researchers considerable freedom of action.

. . . The third feature of the . . . interrelated system is that although policy making has become more centralized, the research

15 *Ibid.*, pp. 97–98.
16 National Academy of Sciences, *Federal Support of Basic Research in Institutions of Higher Learning*, 1964.

effort itself remains highly decentralized and dispersed among many universities.[17]

Both in structure and operation the interrelated system is pluralistic, decentralized, and acts largely through a pressure-group style of decision-making.[18] Although assuming a variety of diverse and marginally related functions, the *service* obligations of the interrelated system constitute its public defense. As one observer has explained, the interrelated system is expected to provide money to departmental and "agency missions, to advance knowledge in certain defined areas of special interest (such as atomic energy, outer space, and the diseases studied by the National Institutes of Health), to subsidize projects in various disciplines, and to promote scientific education." [19] These objectives are anticipated and loosely coordinated at the presidential level by the Bureau of the Budget, the Office of Science and Technology, the Federal Council for Science and Technology, and the President's Science Advisory Committee.[20] Decisions made here, however, are anything but conclusive. They respond instead to incremental influences at work within universities, industry, executive departments and agencies, the National Academy of Sciences, and Congressional committees and subcommittees.

Professionalized science has its greatest input into the interrelated system through the advisory mechanism of such agencies as the National Science Foundation (NSF) and the National Institutes of Health (NIH). As Michael Reagan has suggested: "NSF review panels and NIH study sections (the outsider peer groups that rate particular research proposals) have been "pure

[17] Robert Gilpin, *France in the Age of the Scientific State* (Princeton, N.J.: Princeton University Press, 1968), pp. 133–137.

[18] See Sanford Lakoff's review of Harvey Brooks, *The Government of Science* and Michael Reagan, *Science and the Federal Patron* in the *American Political Science Review* 63, no. 4 (December 1969): 1282. See also H. L. Nieburg, *In the Name of Science* (Chicago: Quadrangle Books, 1966), Chap. 9, "The Emergence of Pluralism," pp. 158–183.

[19] Lakoff, review, *loc. cit.*

[20] Other policy formulating bodies at this level are the National Aeronautics and Space Council, the National Council on Marine Resources and Engineering Development, and the Defense Science Board.

science" bodies; i.e., they have consisted only of scientists and only of those in the field whose proposals were being rated." [21] Within the National Institutes of Health the review procedure for supporting basic research is relatively simple and purposefully weighted in favor of academic scientists. Once an application is received it is assigned to a study section which exercises professional "jurisdiction" over that area. There are approximately fifty study sections in the NIH with the executive secretaries of each section in charge of appointing members.[22] In practice the executive secretaries select prominent members of disciplinary peer groups and on matters of scientific judgment yield to their decisions. After the study sections make their recommendations, the grant requests are sent to the advisory councils of each institute. Unlike the study sections, the councils are statutory bodies composed of twelve members appointed by the Surgeon General. Six members of each council must qualify as leading scientific or medical authorities, but the remainder may be chosen from a variety of leaders in education or public affairs.[23] In most cases the review function of the advisory councils constitutes an endorsement of the reports from the study sections. As a recent governmental survey indicates:

> Relatively rarely, a Council may approve an application which was originally disapproved by the Study Section, and in as many as 3 percent of the cases the Council may disapprove an application approved by the preliminary reviewing group. Almost never does the Council overrule a Study Section purely on a question of scientific merit. If a council member or group of members disagrees seriously with the Study Section, the application may be sent back for reappraisal by the Section but the latter is under no compulsion to revise its original opinion.[24]

The review process of the National Science Foundation functions in a similar way, with almost complete reliance upon the

[21] Michael D. Reagan, *Science and the Federal Patron* (New York: Oxford University Press, 1969), p. 98.

[22] *Biomedical Science and Its Administration: A Study of the National Institutes of Health* (Washington, D.C.: The White House, 1965), p. 193.

[23] *Ibid.*, p. 194.

[24] *Ibid.*

advice of scientists outside the Foundation. Under normal circumstances extramural peer-group evaluation is achieved through the use of two instruments: the ad hoc review and the advisory panel.[25] The ad hoc review is a rather informal procedure whereby leaders in the scientific community are asked to assess individual proposals by mail. The advisory panel, on the other hand, is a part of the formal process of decision-making within the agency; in both structure and composition it enables scientific peer groups to register their judgments on prospective lines of research with force and effectiveness.

Panel members are appointed as consultants to the Foundation by a program director from one of the eleven major scientific program areas.[26] The Foundation has made it clear that "in selecting outside reviewers for a proposal, the program officer seeks experts who are knowledgeable in the specialized scientific subject matter of the proposal and in contemporary work in that field and who are familiar with the principal investigator's past achievement." [27] Thus, the panels intentionally reflect the interests of professionalized science and in most cases panel recommendations go unchallenged. Of course, panel decisions are reviewed by the program director, by his division director,[28] by the Associate Director of Research and by the Grants Office before final submission to the Office of the Director. But a panel commitment carries both the prestige and authority of the scientific community, and it is rarely overridden.

The influence of professionalized science extends throughout the interrelated system, but beyond the confines of NSF and NIH

[25] Subcommittee on Science, Research and Development, House Committee on Science and Astronautics, *Hearings, 1970 National Science Foundation Authorization,* Vol. 2 91st Cong., 1st sess. 1969, p. 27.

[26] The eleven program areas are mathematics, physics, chemistry, biological sciences, astronomy, atmospheric sciences, oceanography, earth sciences, engineering, social sciences, and interdisciplinary research on problems relevant to our society.

[27] Subcommittee on Science, Research and Development, *loc. cit.*

[28] There are six divisions in NSF: Division of Biological and Medical Sciences, Division of Environmental Sciences, Division of Engineering, Division of Mathematical and Physical Sciences, Division of Social Sciences, Office of Sea Grant Programs.

it is limited. Its role, for example, in the Atomic Energy Commission, NASA, and the Department of Defense must be adjusted to organizational missions and economic interests that link the federal government to universities and industry. Within the system both basic and applied science are carried forward, but they are increasingly combined in what is now called "developmental research" — a hybrid activity intended to encourage the creation of new products and techniques that anticipate organizational needs. The pivotal instrument around which these efforts revolve is the government contract, a legal arrangement that enables the federal government to purchase the type of research it desires from universities, industrial firms, and other private research organizations. Not all contracting, of course, is for development, but funds allocated for this category amount to more than two-thirds of the federal budget for "R and D." [29]

The purpose of contracting for development is supposedly to enhance the service capacity of executive departments and agencies. This justification, however, is now largely symbolic, for it is very difficult to determine the precise contributions of developmental research to applied missions. In reality, contracting for development is used almost exclusively as a tool for augmenting the resources of the three institutional components of the interrelated system. In the universities such contracting has provided funds for educational and administrative expansion; in industry it has created a stable market for sophisticated military hardware; and in executive departments and agencies it has supplied the resources for examining "alternative futures" that can affect their objects and goals.

As matters stand, the service capacity of the interrelated system seems hopelessly confused with the ability of its institutions to generate assessments of hypothetical futures and to deploy resources against their possible realization. While this assumption may seem incredible, a recent episode within the Department of Defense offers a clear illustration.[30] In 1955, roughly a year after

[29] See Lakoff, footnote 18.
[30] The following account is paraphrased from Herbert York, "ABM, MIRV, and the Arms Race," *Science* 169 (July 17, 1970): 257.

research had begun on the development of the first United States intercontinental ballistic missile (ICBM), the Army engaged the Bell Telephone Laboratories to make a study on the feasibility of building an antiballistic missile (ABM). After careful investigation, the Bell Laboratories determined that it was indeed possible, and late in 1956 the Nike Zeus project was launched. Subsequent research, however, revealed that missile defense might be made immensely more difficult if missile offense took advantage of several hypothetical "penetration aids." The Defense Department set up a committee to examine this possibility, and in the early part of 1958 the committee reported that missile defense might be seriously handicapped if it were confronted by such offensive devices as decoys, tank fragments, chaff, and multiple warheads. By 1960, the ICBM developers were keenly aware of these prospects and gradually began adapting their hardware to include a new offensive strategy called "multiple independently-targeted reentry vehicles" (MIRV) — which led in turn to the redesign of hypothetical defensive strategies.

Developmental research of this nature has been characterized by Herbert York as a "continuously reciprocating process" sustained by internal interests rather than by the presence of external necessity. In responding to the case just reviewed, York argues that

> early developments of MIRV and ABM were not primarily the result of any careful operations analysis of the problem or of anything which might be described as a "provocation" by the other side. Rather, they were largely the result of a continuously reciprocating process consisting of a technological challenge put out by the designers of our own defense and accepted by the designers of our own offense, then followed by a similar challenge and response sequence in reverse direction.[31]

Although MIRV and ABM were largely the work of applied technology and not the product of basic research, they nevertheless reveal constraints applicable to any scientific or science-related activity within the interrelated system. Thus, when the services of professionalized science are needed, they are directed

[31] *Ibid.*

toward the interests of institutional clients whose primary concern is the anticipation and management of alternative futures.

This tendency deeply affects the internal structure of basic research, for it alters the scope within which the politics of science takes place. Peer group leaders must adjust to demands from a wide range of interests operating within the institutions of the interrelated system. Since these groupings are preoccupied with hypothetical futures, science too tends to take on similar characteristics. In fact, the President of the National Academy of Sciences has clearly addressed himself to this point:

> My own belief is that science remains the most powerful tool we have yet generated to apply leverage for our future. It is the instrument which is most useful for guiding our own destinies, for assuring the condition of man in the years to come. I have much to hope that we will not abandon that tool, leaving us to our own brute devices.[32]

Precisely this attachment to "futures" forces politics within the interrelated system to an intensive preoccupation with budgets and policy commitments — especially those that relate to the allocation and use of scientific resources. Budgets are primarily concerned with the establishment of funding levels and it seems clear that they directly affect the composition of research in three ways: they influence the choice of fields that receive the greatest support; they encourage the discovery of new phenomena by providing for the construction of expensive instruments; and they designate particular types of research to be performed.

One of the purest manifestations of "field-support" politics appeared in 1962 with the creation of a special Committee on Science and Public Policy (COSPUP) within the National Academy of Sciences.[33] The idea behind the committee had been ad-

---

[32] Subcommittee on Science, Research and Development, House Committee on Science and Astronautics, *Hearings, 1971 National Science Foundation Authorization*, 91st Cong. 2nd sess., 1970, p. 16, testimony of Philip Handler.

[33] The account that follows is heavily dependent upon two sources of information: Greenberg, *The Politics of Pure Science*, pp. 160–169; and Kenneth Kofmehl, "COSPUP, Congress and Scientific Advice," *Journal of*

vanced by George B. Kistiakowsky, an internationally recognized
chemist who was both an Academy member and a former presidential science adviser. Put briefly, Kistiakowsky wanted to
create a unique "lobbying arm" that would address itself to questions concerning levels of support for basic research. As Greenberg has observed:

> What Kistiakowsky was particularly interested in was that
> COSPUP should serve as a scholarly, dignified advocate for re-
> search by producing inventories of the scientific status of various
> fields and assessing the resources required to follow promising
> lines of inquiries. It was his belief that persuasive argument was
> the best weapon available to the profession. . . . Finally, it is also
> worth noting that Kistiakowsky had arrived at an informal un-
> derstanding with Kennedy's science adviser, Jerome Wiesner.
> When COSPUP came forth with a study, it was agreed, the
> White House science advisory apparatus would seriously con-
> sider the data and recommendations. Since Kistiakowsky was a
> member of the President's Science Advisory Committee (PSAC),
> and the staff serving PSAC had close ties to the Bureau of the
> Budget, the informal Kistiakowsky-Wiesner agreement . . . had
> a good deal of practical significance in the political affairs of sci-
> ence. In a sense, the arrangement was not too different from hav-
> ing a loan applicant at a bank serve as adviser to the loan officer
> handling his application.[34]

With great tact Kistiakowsky invited members of the scientific
community to use COSPUP in attempting to justify federal support. The first group to show an interest was the professional
chemists who had long felt that the federal government discouraged research opportunities by refusing to increase its share
of the science budget.[35] Under the guidance of COSPUP a committee was established to survey the entire field of chemistry,
using funds supplied for the purpose by the National Science

Politics 28 (February 1966): pp. 100–120. Kofmehl's essay is particularly rewarding, for it contains a penetrating description of the relationship among
COSPUP, Congress, and the science advisory mechanisms of the presidency.

[34] Greenberg, *The Politics of Pure Science,* pp. 160–161.

[35] *Ibid.,* p. 156.

Foundation and the American Chemical Society.[36] After a careful and comprehensive review, the committee reported that the viability of chemical research would be seriously threatened if the federal government did not substantially increase its allocations. In Greenberg's words:

> It concluded that in chemistry, great scientific opportunities were being thwarted by unmet financial needs. The product of the . . . survey was a striking example of advocacy attired in the dispassionate, nonpolemical methodology of science. But the case it made was a compelling one — so compelling, in fact, that the government of science could not help but listen. . . .[37]

Although massive and persuasive, the report was not taken at face value. As is characteristic of budgetary politics in the interrelated system, the report was evaluated by an interagency committee at the presidential level, which proved to be less than sympathetic. The committee stood firm in its assessment, but the matter was passed along to Congress and to other executive agencies for further consideration. This meant that the phalanx of chemists working around COSPUP had an additional opportunity to apply leverage at subsequent decision points. As anticipated, they met the occasion with as much enthusiasm and dedication as had characterized their earlier survey of the discipline. Finally, under pressure, the NSF did agree to a sizeable budgetary increase. But other agencies, responding to competing interests, chose to continue their support within the guidelines established by previous allocations.

Perhaps more visible than the politics of disciplinary support are attempts by the scientific community to secure important research instruments that represent major capital investments. Particle accelerators are a case in point, for not only do they make possible a view of reality that could not be attained without them, but obtaining funds for their construction involves an interplay of economic, political, and military interests. The decision, for example, to build the 200-bev. accelerator at Batavia, Illinois, was sensitive to pressures that began with its design at the Lawrence

[36] *Ibid.*, p. 162.
[37] *Ibid.*, p. 163.

Radiation Laboratory (Berkeley) and encompassed — over several turbulent years — the interests of the Atomic Energy Commission, the Joint Committee on Atomic Energy, the science advisory mechanisms of the presidency, Midwestern scientists and politicians, university representatives, prominent industrialists, and the Department of Defense. The opportunity to learn more about the structure of matter was therefore dependent not upon an interest in scientific discovery, but upon political forces concerned with budgets, defense, and the equitable geographical distribution of federal resources. The Midwest, in particular, was eager for the machine to be built, provided it could be located somewhere within the region. The Johnson administration first decided against the area, primarily because the Argonne National Laboratory was already operating a smaller accelerator there. But in 1966 with presidential attention preoccupied with Vietnam, the Atomic Energy Commission yielded to pressures from both scientists and politicians and approved a construction site less than thirty miles from the Argonne research center itself.[38]

A third feature of "budgetary politics" is the restriction of funds to particular types of research. Allocations of this nature are generally made to support departmental and agency missions, such as those in health, education, and defense. By definition, missions are organized to deal with concrete problems that the political process has found it necessary to institutionalize. Consequently, when attempts are made to re-examine research priorities, missions become the focal point for both public and private interests having a stake in the final outcome. As far as basic research is concerned, missions have had two important effects: they have helped create research problems instrumental to departmental and agency goals (for example, the support of immunization research to improve the quality of health care); and they have frequently encouraged research with no immediate application, which may, at some future time, hold the key to agency or departmental success. In this way there is a tendency within applied missions for alliances to be built among prospective funding agencies and that part of the scientific community which

[38] *Ibid.*, p. 269.

receives support. Because they are mutually advantageous, the alliances form an important control mechanism within the interrelated system — a control whereby research interests modify departmental and agency perceptions and they, in turn, influence the direction of research. This appears to be Philip Handler's criticism of current restrictions upon the use of defense appropriations:

> I rather regret the passage of that amendment [the Mansfield amendment, limiting the use of defense funds to research projects that have a direct bearing on military activity], but I would put the problem in somewhat different terms than some of my colleagues. Some of our colleagues on university campuses have found no trouble with this amendment. They regret the loss of funds, but don't regret the fact that funds would no longer be forthcoming from the military to support, on campus, fundamental research. I regret the latter. I am troubled by the fact that a barrier may be interposed between the academic-scientific community and the Department of Defense. I cannot conceive that that serves the national interest. . . . In the national interest, there should be a continuing dialog between the academic community and the Department of Defense. It provides a mechanism whereby some portion of the civilian part of our society maintains a watchful eye on what is going on on the military side. It provides one element of our traditional civilian control of the military.[39]

Although budgetary politics affects the *composition* of basic research, concern within the scientific community for matters of national policy reflects an interest in the *use* to which scientific knowledge or science-related technologies may be put. In this sense, portions of the scientific community have been advocates of "hypothetical futures" from the time Einstein sent his A-bomb letter to President Roosevelt.[40] Not until after the Second World War, however, did a pattern emerge where scientists would be enlisted to work for changes in national policy. The first impulse in this direction came within the scientific community from sci-

[39] See footnote 32.
[40] See Ralph Lapp, *The New Priesthood* (New York: Harper and Row, 1965), p. 180.

entists who had worked on the atomic bomb. The issue that held the group together and served to focus its energies was the possibility of civilian control of atomic energy. To increase their effectiveness the scientists created the Federation of Atomic Scientists, whose purpose was to bring scientific expertise to bear upon key Congressional committees and to educate the public at large. Their efforts had twofold results: on one hand, they were successful in getting the control of atomic energy placed in the hands of a civilian agency (the Atomic Energy Commission); on the other, they exposed the organizational weaknesses of the scientific community and revealed the vulnerability of scientific judgment on matters of public policy. Ralph Lapp explains:

> The "victory" of the scientists in backing the McMahon bill [the bill to create the Atomic Energy Commission] was not won without losses. The initial display of scientists before congressional committees demonstrated that these men had feet of clay, and shrewd politicians noted the fact with some relish. In addition, the scientists showed that they did not have a tightly knit community ruled over by a single High Priest or even by a clique of leaders with one mind. There was great diversity in the loose assembly of scientists, and no one person could pretend to speak for all of science.[41]

The political strategy of the atomic scientists — that scientific expertise could be used as a persuasive instrument of policy — has become a routine part of political maneuver in the interrelated system. Moreover, scientific prediction and assessment — including the active participation of scientists themselves — have stamped interest-group competition with a high degree of sophistication. In fact, conflicting scientific claims are widely used (and sometimes even generated) by powerful institutions in their struggle over access to future resources.

One of the most controversial issues to divide the scientific community and bring out conflicting judgments over scientific

---

[41] *Ibid.*, p. 102. For a much more elaborate account of the Atomic Scientists' Movement see Alice Kimball Smith, *A Peril and a Hope* (Chicago: University of Chicago Press, 1965).

merit was the proposed deployment of an antiballistic missile system. In the spring of 1969 the Department of Defense and the Subcommittee on International Organization and Disarmament Affairs of the Senate Foreign Relations Committee publicly displayed their talent for using scientific testimony in support of differing strategic policies. But the Foreign Relations subcommittee did so with a directness that deserves special notice. In preparing for the ABM debate the Subcommittee recruited three witnesses of commanding prestige from the professional scientific community: James Killian, Chairman of the Board at Massachusetts Institute of Technology and one of Eisenhower's science advisers; George Kistiakowsky, professor of chemistry at Harvard and also a former presidential science adviser; and Herbert York, a physicist from the University of California at San Diego and former Director of Defense Research and Engineering. Since the hearings were nationally televised, the Subcommittee wasted little time with introductory or technical questions and moved quickly to ask for an assessment of the strategic implications of the ABM. Here is a sample of the testimony:

Senator Fulbright. . . . you say that the deployment of Nike X or the Sentinel system could actually be harmful to our national security. Instead of being an addition to it, it is harmful. Did I understand you correctly?

Dr. Kistiakowsky. Yes, sir; you understood me quite correctly. I think it is a very serious possibility, and the reasons for that, as I have discussed in my, of course, very condensed statement, are possibilities for an accelerated arms race, with the consequent loss of secure deterrent which we have now.

Furthermore, and I think this should not be disregarded, is the commitment of the ever-increasing funds which such an arms race would entail and with it the terrible harm to our society at home, and the dangers of further militarization of our society. All of these factors, I think, are of great importance and by no means idle speculation.

Senator Fulbright. This was a point on which I thought you were all in general agreement. I believe, Dr. York, you also said that to deploy this system would jeopardize our security rather than improve it; did you not?

Dr. York. Yes, and for the same basic reasons.

Senator Fulbright. Yes.

Dr. York. That it is an element in heating up the arms race; that it, in fact, may mislead people into thinking they are safer than they are and, therefore, making riskier decisions.

Senator Fulbright. I thought it was very clear that both of you said it.

Do you agree, Dr. Killian, with that same conclusion? You did not make it quite as clear, but you agree?

Dr. Killian. I tried to make it clear.

Senator Fulbright. Is it fair to say that all three of you agree on that point?

Dr. Killian. The action is conditioned by fear of escalation.

Senator Fulbright. All three of you, three of the most eminent scientists, then, agree that to deploy this system would jeopardize our security at the present time; is that correct?

Dr. York. It is a step in the wrong direction.

Dr. Kistiakowsky. Yes.

Senator Fulbright. It is remarkable that there is this unanimity of view of men of your stature, and yet we are faced with the possibility that even today or tomorrow a decision may be made to deploy it. It is a rather remarkable situation.

I do not believe that they will make that decision. I cannot bring myself to believe it, but anyway it could happen. It is a possibility.[42]

It is true, of course, that the scientists testifying before the Subcommittee knew they were being used to bolster a particular policy position and willingly lent their prestige to resist a "future" they considered impractical and unnecessary. In many cases, however, there is little awareness of how "policy politics" employs or conditions scientific judgment. Take, for example, the conflict between the National Science Foundation and the Department of Defense over the relation between pure research and applied technology. The dispute arose primarily because the Johnson administration was developing a science policy that emphasized the application of research to anticipated social prob-

[42] Subcommittee on International Organization and Disarmament Affairs, Senate Committee on Foreign Relations, *Hearings, The Strategic and Foreign Policy Implications of Antiballistic Missile Systems*, 91st Cong., 1st sess., 1969), pp. 92–93.

lems.[43] To provide guidelines for this policy, the Defense Department commissioned a study to explore the linkage between basic research and technological innovations. Published in 1966 as *Project Hindsight*, the report concluded that since 1945, basic research had contributed insignificantly to the technical problems of defense.[44] The National Science Foundation was instantly' shaken, for *Hindsight* threatened its future capacity to support nonapplied research. In an effort to counter the Defense Department the Foundation asked the Research Institute of the Illinois Institute of Technology to carry out a similar study. Once the project had been completed, the assessment released by NSF — *Technology in Retrospect and Critical Events in Science* (TRACES) — was a masterpiece of institutional strategy. It did not refute the findings of *Hindsight* but suggested instead that the Department of Defense had not gone far enough back in its examination of basic research.[45] In fact, TRACES discovered that roughly 90 per cent of the basic research responsible for an innovation occurred at least a decade in advance. The implication of the finding was quite clear: a science policy devoted largely to applied research might jeopardize the nation's technological future.

Although the scientific community may never appreciate the extent to which institutional demands condition or manipulate scientific judgment,[46] there are indications that some scientists

[43] See Philip M. Boffey, "The Hornig Years: Did LBJ Neglect His Science Adviser? *Science* 163 (January 31, 1969): 454.

[44] Peter Thompson, "TRACES: Basic Research Links to Technology Appraised," *Science* 163 (January 24, 1969): 374.

[45] *Ibid.*

[46] Recently, the Center for Science in the Public Interest uncovered two cases that further show how institutional commitment affects the evaluation of scientific evidence. As reported in *Science:*

. . . the Department of Health, Education, and Welfare and Allied Chemical Corporation conducted separate tests this year to determine the levels of mercury in urine samples taken from workers at Allied's chlorine and caustic soda plant in Moundsville, W. Va. The government's tests (now being challenged by the company) revealed about three times as much mercury as the company's tests.

In another case . . . the Bureau of Mines (BOM), with the help of the American Petroleum Institute (API), conducted tests comparing leaded and nonleaded gasoline. The tests indicated that nonleaded fuel

wish to assume a more active role in developing policy alternatives. As one "activist" has put it: "When you have a disinterested academy in a very interested world, you have disaster." [47]
Yet attempts thus far to reframe policy options have been fragmented and sporadic. "Teach-ins" and research "strikes" have
been staged,[48] but it is difficult to measure their impact. Perhaps a
more significant development is the growing policy consciousness of several scientific associations. Many professional societies,
perhaps for the first time, are being asked by some of their members to assume a more forceful role in confronting society's problems. In a recent meeting of the American Physical Society, for
example, petitions were circulated against the war in Vietnam,
protests were directed against the supersonic transport, and a re-
quest was made that the association discourage acceptance of
research support from the Department of Defense.[49] The widely
read *Chemical and Engineering News* of the American Chemical
Society has given its approval to efforts by chemists to halt the
spread of war in Asia and to remove the ROTC from university
campuses. According to its editor:

> Some of the activity will doubtless prove to be misguided and
> inappropriate. But the important thing is that people may be
> moving away from a let-Jack-do-it philosophy on the one hand
> and toward action within our system on the other. And that,
> after all, is what this country is all about.[50]

---

would have adverse effects on air quality because other necessary ad-
ditives would give it a "higher photochemical pollution potential." These
results have been attacked by the Air Pollution Control Administration,
which said that BOM "functioned as a contractor working under the
direction of an API task force" and that the API selected the fuels and
other variables to be used in the experiments.

Constance Holden, "Public Interest: New Group Seeks Redefinition of
Scientists' Role," *Science* 173, no. 3992 (July 9, 1971): 132.

[47] Statement from Howard Zinn (Boston University) in Bryce Nelson,
"MIT's March 4: Scientists Discuss Renouncing Military Research," *Science* 169 (March 14, 1969): 1175.

[48] *Ibid.*

[49] *Physics Today* 23, no. 3 (March 1970): 67.

[50] *Chemical and Engineering News* 48, no. 21 (May 18, 1970): 3.

Even the cautious editorial position of *Science* has been affected by these developments. Its influential editor points out:

> A few decades ago, most scientists held the view that their principal duty was to advance the frontiers of knowledge. Correspondingly, the scientific societies limited their activities to publications and meetings centered on their chosen fields. During the past few years, the activities of scientists have expanded. . . . [Yet] scientists have not unanimously approved participation in policy matters by their colleagues. Some have objected that spokesmen certainly did not speak for them personally. Others have pointed out that once facts have become generally known, the scientist can no longer determine how his discoveries may be applied. To some degree, this argument is valid. Nevertheless, scientists will have continuing and important roles in determining how science is applied. One important function is that of watchdog.[51]

It is difficult for many scientists to accept the professional society as a legitimate critic and designer of public policies. One chemist told *Chemical and Engineering News:*

> . . . I object to your abuse of space in our publications to discuss your private opinions on political, social, and military matters. If you wish to express them privately, that is your business, but I think you are out of order to speak for the Society. . . . I suggest you confine your contributions to the subject for which the journal was intended. Its name is *Chemical and Engineering News,* and there are unlimited scientific subjects to discuss editorially.[52]

Another frequent reservation is that policy-active professions may not be tolerant of opposing points of view — a fear that may be rooted in an awareness of how these institutions act on purely scientific matters. Writing to *Science*, a mathematician confronted this issue directly:

> Scientists are being systematically urged to ask their professional societies to take a stand against the war in Indochina. I wish to

[51] "Social Responsibilities of Scientists," *Science* 167 (January 16, 1970): 241.

[52] Letter from E. R. Gustafson (Chicago, Ill.), *Chemical and Engineering News* 48 (June 22, 1970): 7.

point out that the avoidance of such stands is a matter of principle, not just tradition. If a society to which I belong takes stands on non-scientific issues, it will sooner or later espouse one that is abhorrent to me, forcing me to condone it or resign. Eventually the society will be reduced to a small, politically single-minded group. This group will then have succeeded, intentionally or not, in suppressing all political thought except its own.[53]

Perhaps the greatest fear is that policy-conscious professions will intrude upon the survival and expansion interests of the major power institutions. It is widely believed that this may mean diminished opportunities for independent research. Although the "activists" do not reject this argument, they suspect that it may be anachronistic. In fact, much of their concern for policy alternatives rests upon the belief that research is already shaped to a large degree by external forces. Thus, to fulfill their responsibilities, science professions must be prepared to confront a new institutional order — one not only research reliant but oriented toward the politics of policy projects.[54]

The Postindustrial State. The present conflict and uncertainty within the professional scientific community may be a response to some indications — very early indications — of another shift in political power. Of course, it may be hazardous to speculate about an uncompleted development, but the power alignments of the bureaucratic state appear to be altered. Perhaps the most prominent feature of this change is a further expansion of the public realm — although not in the sense of enlarging the service, regulatory, or ownership functions of the central government. What seems to have happened is that the conglomerate activities of the bureaucratic state have served as so many nuclei for building institutional complexes out of previously distinct public and private interests. It is common, for example, to attribute influen-

[53] Letter from Robert Hooke (Pittsburgh, Pa.), *Science* 169 (July 17, 1970): 234–235.

[54] The phrase "research reliant" comes from James R. Killian, Jr., "Toward a Research Reliant Society: Some Observations on Government and Science" in Harry Woolf, ed., *Science as a Cultural Force* (Baltimore: The Johns Hopkins Press, 1964).

tial activities to the military-industrial complex, the techno-scientific complex, the communications complex, and the service and regulatory complexes of the federal government. But what is frequently missed in the use of these terms is the realization that they refer to a new kind of *public* entity — a new institutional cluster of influence and expertise.

Lowi has described many aspects of complexes with his term "interest-group liberalism" — a view that stresses the corporate exercise of power by private interest groups and governmental institutions.[55] As used here, the word *complexes* refers to loosely coordinated centers of decision-making, involving both public and private components, that engage in activities of national scope. The institutions connected with pesticide policy provide an illustration. In addition to the input of large chemical firms from the private sector (for example, American Cyanamid, Dow, Du Pont, Eli Lilly, Union Carbide, Rohm and Haas, Upjohn, and Velsicol), decisions affecting the registration and use of pesticides are influenced by the Agricultural Research Service of the Department of Agriculture, the Fish and Wildlife Service of the Department of Interior, the Food and Drug Administration, the Public Health Service, and the Environmental Protection Agency.

In the postindustrial state, one can argue that complexes make up the viable units of political power. To maintain their positions they appropriate many resources of the bureaucratic state and use them for growth and protection. Under such circumstances professionalized science is regarded simply as another instrument for aggregating resources and may be employed for a wide variety of unrelated tasks.

The stress that this places upon professional identity and the degree to which it affects peer group judgment are presumed to be great. Perhaps Don Price has caught a glimpse of this trend in using the term "estate" to describe the enlarged activities of science, but it is Toulmin who has shown that science may have even more amorphous characteristics — that it can be applied against any need or used to anticipate any contingency. In the postindustrial state, these features are so pervasive that they force

[55] Theodore J. Lowi, *The End of Liberalism* (New York: W. W. Norton, 1969), p. 71.

a new description of the scientific enterprise. The interrelated system with its subtle connection between public and private interests must now confront an *instrumental system* in which science is manipulated by powerful complexes.

The instrumental system does not rely upon the contract for allocating resources or planning research; it relies instead upon the policy project or program. Projects are attempts to appropriate future resources by identifying social problems or needs and defining them in such a way that the expertise of the complex is thought necessary to their solution. (In fact, one might suggest that the present mood of social crisis is to some extent related to these developments.) It is true that several complexes may compete for the anticipated resources of a single project. The educational and welfare complexes, for example, may be drawn into competition by the prospects of a war on poverty or a Model Cities program; the techno-scientific complex may challenge the military-industrial complex or the regulatory complexes for projects involving the domestic use of atomic energy or fighting environmental pollution.

The scope of decision-making within the instrumental system is exceedingly wide and depends upon so many sources of information that no single group can competently exercise the responsibility. Decisions are reached, to be sure, but they result from an almost endless process of "digesting or exchanging and testing information." [56] The typical pattern is for a number of committees — each exercising a unique competence — to steer decisions to the degree that its expertise is relevant. Although there is no recognizable center of command and control, a guidance mechanism does exist for evaluating expansion opportunities with the greatest possible information. The guidance feature is supplied by what Galbraith has called the "technostructure," a device for the cybernetic ordering of institutional expertise. He explains:

> Guidance . . . consists of numerous individuals who are engaged, at any given time, in obtaining, digesting or exchanging and testing information. A very large part of the exchange and testing of

[56] John Kenneth Galbraith, *The New Industrial State* (New York: The New American Library, 1968), p. 74.

information is by word-of-mouth — a discussion in an office, at
lunch or over the telephone. But the most typical procedure is
through the committee and the committee meeting. . . . Committee discussion enables members to pool information under
circumstances which allow, also, of immediate probing to assess
the relevance and reliability of the information offered. . . . The
groups are numerous, as often informal as formal, and subject to
constant change in composition. Each contains the men possessed
of the information, or with access to the information, that bears
on the particular decision together with those whose skill consists
in extracting and testing this information and obtaining a conclusion.[57]

As the guidance mechanism for the instrumental system, the
scientific technostructure is manipulated by what the powerful
complexes anticipate as necessary for gaining access to future
resources. The kind of science fostered under these arrangements
is not committed to discovery or to service to society, but rather
to projects or programs aimed at accumulating and developing
institutional resources (see Table 5.1). An awareness of these
conditions has led several scientific disciplines — and militant scientists everywhere — to recommend alternative projects for scientific work.[58] But the significance of these proposals has thus far
been marginal. The instrumental system is not sensitive to the
weak and unorganized; it responds only to the power of com-

[57] *Ibid.,* pp. 74–76.

[58] The proposal for a research strike by faculty members of the M.I.T.
physics department clearly illustrates what I mean. . . . Among the points
which the faculty endorsed were:

1. To devise means for turning research applications away from the
present overemphasis on military technology towards the solution of
pressing environmental and social problems;

2. To convey to our students the hope that they will devote themselves
to bringing the benefits of science and technology to mankind, and to ask
them to scrutinize the issues raised here before participating in the construction of destructive weapons systems;

3. To express our determined opposition to ill-advised and hazardous
projects such as the ABM system, the enlargement of our nuclear arsenal,
and the development of chemical and biological weapons.

See Bryce Nelson, "Scientists Plan Research Strike, at MIT on 4 March,"
Science 163 (January 24, 1969): 373.

Table 5.1 SPATIAL AND FUNCTIONAL CHARACTERISTICS OF SCIENCE IN RELATION TO CONFIGURATIONS OF POLITICAL POWER

	Organization of Political Power		
	Liberal state	Bureaucratic state	Postindustrial state
System of science	autonomous	interrelated	instrumental
Mode of decision making	peer group	interest group	technostructure
Mode of research allocation	grant	contract	policy project (or program)
Relationship between allocator and recipient	patron	client	employer
Organizational goal	discovery	service	growth
Representatives	Polanyi	Weinberg, Price	Toulmin

plexes and the politics of growth. Yet the protests may have an unanticipated value. By questioning the use of scientific resources, they may ultimately call attention to the relation between the institutions of political power and the politics of research. Perhaps the effect of this discovery will be less than anticipated here, but at the very least it should raise doubts about forms of scientific inquiry that claim to be independent of social and political influence. It is hoped this realization will not be interpreted negatively, for we have much to gain from an appreciation of how institutional activity refines and extends our perceptions of reality.

Appendix A

Research design and methodology

THE INITIAL PHASE of this study was an inductive survey covering a number of actual research environments. The investigation was undertaken on the hopeful assumption that previous studies of professionalization could perhaps be supplemented by a fresh empirical view. As the research proceeded, what began to appear was not so much data additional to earlier efforts as an exercise in cognitive discovery. Patterns of interpersonal dynamics as well as aspects of organizational structure afforded some new perspectives on the role of politics in the extension and validation of scientific perception.

The project was launched during the summer of 1967 as a series of unstructured interviews with scientists of outstanding reputation who were conducting research at the University of California at Berkeley. About half the scientists selected for study could not spare the time for an interview, and were replaced by scientists whose accomplishments were not so impressive, but whose research was respectable. Subsequent interviews included scientists at the University of Texas and at Purdue. A provisional schedule of questions was prepared before each interview, although it was difficult to confine more imaginative scientists to this artificial format. The more eminent the scientist, the more difficult it was to hold him to the schedule of topics. One Nobel Laureate, after completing a lengthy discussion, complained: "I know you're not here to interview me about this, but perhaps you should be." A much more unrestrained response characterized an interview with a world-famous mathematician. A man of activist political sympathies, he broke violently into several of our questions about the role of the scientist as a synthesizer of scientific knowledge to make such comments as:

> I don't give a damn about this. It's off base. It's wide of the mark. Scientists aren't concerned with an epistemological tradition. The creative ones don't give a damn about the past. All of us are trapped by the present. That's just the way it is. You don't make a scientific discovery by thinking about the epistemic conventions of science. Science is what scientists are *doing* at the moment.

Despite occasional setbacks of this nature most of the interviews dealt with a variety of issues subsumed under the following themes:

1. The scope of professional identity.
2. Disciplinary patterns of information exchange.
3. The control function of professional journals.
4. The impact of research specialization on the theoretical structure of science.
5. The norms of scientific research.
6. The nature of scientific disputes.
7. The role of "opinion leaders" in scientific research.
8. The distinction between pure and applied research.
9. The contact of science with larger society (including the government).

The scientists did not always comment with the same rigor and simplicity that characterize their professional contributions. Each did insist that he was being honest — a posture that I soon discovered could mean anything from criticizing his colleagues to a self-assertive bluntness. The interviews generally took place in a laboratory setting and varied from forty-five minutes to an hour and a half, depending upon previous commitments of the scientist and the interest he developed in the topics discussed.

To ensure continuity of discussion, the interview sample was prepared in advance and a schedule of topics was developed that could be carried from one specialty to another. When possible, the original sample was supplemented by exchanges with scientists whose work had been either highly praised or roundly condemned by those interviewed earlier. The results were a fascinating combination of expectation and surprise, suggesting that further work should try to reach a greater sample of scientists from more diversified institutions.

The scope of the study was eventually widened, but the original sample provided a number of useful perspectives on the structure and process of scientific knowledge. Table A.1 gives a profile of this group, including their honorific distinctions, but it can scarcely convey the insight and flavor of the interviews themselves. Table A.2 enlarges the profile to include interviews at the University of Texas at Austin and Purdue University.

The "depth" interviews provided an excellent introduction to the behavior of research scientists, for not only were a number of intriguing areas of interpersonal dynamics uncovered, but those interviewed responded with enthusiastic encouragement to the prospects of an empirical study of scientific inquiry. Many scientists quickly pointed out how useless they felt the *philosophy of science* to be and offered suggestions about more reliable ways of exploring the essential features of research activity. Most of their proposals, however, were based on the premise that ample research funds could be secured and that the only conceivable obstacles were those of *sampling* and *data interpretation*.

The immediate problem was selecting a technique which would require modest financial support, but which could also reach a significant portion of the scientific community. The most practical method, it seemed, was to make use of the survey questionnaire and to canvass several fields of scientific expertise. But how was the sample to be drawn? And what specific kinds of information should be sought?

After a careful examination of the formal characteristics of the scientific community, it was decided to draw a stratified sample

Table A.1   Field, Status, and Age of "Depth" Sample from the University of California at Berkeley

Scientific field	University faculty	Age				Type of Work			High Honors	
		Under 30	30–40	40–50	Over 50	Administration	Teaching-research	Research	Nobel prize	Fields award
Mathematics	2		2				2			
Statistics	1				1	1				1
Total formal sciences	3		2		1	1	2			1
Theoretical physics	7	1	1	3	2	3	3	1	1	
Molecular biology	2			2				2		
Biochemistry	2		1	1		1		2		
Chemistry	3		1	1	1	1		2	1	
Physiology	1			1		1				
Zoology	1			1				1		
Total all sciences	19	1	5	9	4	7	5	8	2	1

Table A.2 FIELD, STATUS, AND AGE OF "DEPTH" SAMPLE FROM THE UNIVERSITY OF TEXAS AT AUSTIN AND PURDUE UNIVERSITY

Scientific field	University faculty	Age				Type of Work		
		Under 30	30–40	40–50	Over 50	Administration	Teaching-research	Research
Statistics	1		1					1
Theoretical physics	4		3	1		1		3
Molecular biology	1			1				1
Biochemistry	2		2					2
Chemistry	2		1		1			2
Total	10		7	2	1	1		9

that would subdivide the universe of American scientists into three populations, those in private research corporations, national research laboratories, and public and private universities. These groups, of course, were still too large for total survey and needed further stratification. For the pretest questionnaire, the private research members were limited to a small percentage of scientists drawn from the Du Pont and Bell laboratories. Those in national laboratories were confined to the National Bureau of Standards and the Oak Ridge National Laboratory. Since the "depth" interviews had already given an indication of university opinion, the only academic institution selected for pretesting was Purdue. This choice was made on the assumption that if there were contrasts between large universities of high prestige and those of moderate standing, they might be visible here.

Once the mailing lists for the pretests had been compiled, the questionnaire itself had to be worked into presentable form. The "depth" interviews had pointed to many significant areas of professionalized knowledge, but an extensive effort was made to examine the most important books and articles on the scientific community written within the previous five-year period. This information yielded a provisional questionnaire of 107 items. These questions were then divided into nine categories of analytical interest, and further reductions brought the number of questions to thirty-two.

After reviewing criticisms received from the pretest survey, we prepared a revised questionnaire. Although no substantive changes were introduced, several questions were reworded to ensure greater clarity and precision of meaning. The distribution of the final version was planned for the *entire* scientific staffs of the two private and two national research laboratories (already partially probed by the pretest sample) and a projected panel of public and private universities. But lack of clerical assistance and financial support ultimately confined the statistical universe to the universities alone.

To provide a measure of attitudes within traditional scientific disciplines (mathematics, physics, astronomy, chemistry, biology, and geology), a sample was devised that divided public and private universities in the United States into three strata of high, medium, and low prestige. Four criteria were used to determine the high-prestige stratum: universities most heavily represented over time on the President's Science Advisory Committee, universities receiving the largest percentage of Research and Development grants, universities within which Nobel prize-winning research had occurred at least three times, and professional rankings of university performance as found in Allen M. Cartter, *An Assessment of Quality in Graduate Education* (Washington, D.C.: American Council on Education, 1966). The medium-prestige stratum was determined by selecting universities that had been ranked as "good" by the Cartter survey for three of the traditional fields and had not been listed under more than one of the high prestige criteria. Under this scheme, the high and medium strata accounted for 67 institutions out of a total universe of 1,058. All remaining universities were placed within the low-prestige group.

Due to budgetary constraints only ten universities could be sampled. Five were allocated to the high-prestige stratum, one to the medium, and four to the low-prestige group. For each stratum, random methods were used to select the sample, with the following results:

High Prestige	*Medium Prestige*	*Low Prestige*
University of California (Berkeley)	Washington University (St. Louis)	University of Georgia
Harvard University		University of Nebraska (Lincoln)
California Institute of Technology		University of Arizona
Princeton University		University of Idaho
Stanford University		

Questions were formulated and sent during the spring of 1968 to 1,500 scientists from the ten universities of the sampling frame. In each case only those scientists were polled whose names were listed under the six traditional fields of research. Of the total questionnaires sent, 854 were returned and statistically analyzed.

Nine categories of analytical interest were explored by the following questions in the survey.

1. The Organization of Science
   Questions 10, 14, 17
2. The Social Dynamics of Scientific Research
   Questions 2, 4, 7, 8, 9, 21, 22, 24, 25, 30
3. Patterns of Individual Motivation
   Question 33
4. The Relationship between Science and Larger Society
   Questions 11, 12, 13, 15, 16, 19, 26, 28, 29, 31
5. The Norms of Science
   Questions 24, 25, 29, 30, 31, 32
6. Factors Contributing to Professional Success
   Question 18
7. The Communication Patterns within the Scientific Community
   Questions 1, 20, 29, 30
8. Methodological Problems in Science
   Questions 5, 6, 27
9. Science as a Competitive Knowledge System
   Question 23

The complete questionnaire follows.

Appendix B

The questionnaire

A. *Background Data*
   Year of birth
   Field of specialization

   Year of degree(s) and name of school(s) awarding degree:
Degree	*Year of Degree*	*School*
B.A., B.S., etc.		
M.A., M.S., etc.		
Ph.D.		
Other		

   Is your present position primarily
   1. *administrative*   2. *research*   3. *teaching-research?*
   (Check one of the above.)

B. The statements that follow [1] are found in the literature dealing with the natural sciences and the relationship of these disciplines to the political community at large. Since many nonscientists make contributions to this literature, some questions may appear impres-

---

[1] Those researchers interested in a breakdown by percentage of the answers received from the questionnaire should write to the author, c/o The Lyndon B. Johnson School of Public Affairs, The University of Texas, Austin, Texas 78712.

sionistic. Nevertheless the Committee asks that you check your overall reaction to each question.

1. For science to be advanced it is not enough that fruitful ideas be originated, or new experiments developed, or new methods instituted; the innovations must be effectively *communicated* to others.

   1. *strongly agree*   2. *agree*   3. *can't say*   4. *disagree*
   5. *strongly disagree*

2. Much research in science is undertaken because the project lends itself to the construction of a fashionable research tool or because financial support can be readily achieved.

   1. *strongly agree*   2. *agree*   3. *can't say*   4. *disagree*
   5. *strongly disagree*

3. A substantial part of the intellectual conflict in American science is rooted in issues that are methodological in character.

   1. *strongly agree*   2. *agree*   3. *can't say*   4. *disagree*
   5. *strongly disagree*

4. Within my discipline there has developed an inner group which, in large part, controls the key panel assignments at the annual association meetings.

   1. *strongly agree*   2. *agree*   3. *can't say*   4. *disagree*
   5. *strongly disagree*

5. Revolutions in science (e.g., the displacement of classical mechanics by quantum mechanics to explain the behavior of subatomic particles) are mostly internal revolutions, begun by one or more scientists and then recommended by the initiators to the scientific community at large.

   1. *strongly agree*   2. *agree*   3. *can't say*   4. *disagree*
   5. *strongly disagree*

6. The modern ideal of science is to establish a precise statement of the relationship between and among the data or observed facts; it is not to uncover an unseen reality.

   1. *strongly agree*   2. *agree*   3. *can't say*   4. *disagree*
   5. *strongly disagree*

7. In papers co-authored by men of decidedly unequal reputations, or in findings submitted independently by a scientist of great repute and one not widely known, the man who is best known gets more credit than the other(s).

   1. *strongly agree*   2. *agree*   3. *can't say*   4. *disagree*
   5. *strongly disagree*

8. Within my discipline there is a small group (consistently representing a smaller cluster of universities and research labs) who highly influence what kinds of evidence are acceptable for the empirical confirmation of hypotheses.

   1. *strongly agree*   2. *agree*   3. *can't say*   4. *disagree*
   5. *strongly disagree*

9. If you accept the idea of a small, powerful group in your discipline (see question 8), what would you estimate the number of influential men to be?

   1. *less than 10*   2. *10–15*   3. *20–30*   4. *40–50*
   5. *more than 50*

10. The pursuit of science is best organized when as much freedom as possible is granted to all scientists.

    1. *strongly agree*   2. *agree*   3. *can't say*   4. *disagree*
    5. *strongly disagree*

11. Public support for basic research is largely due to the belief that utilizable results will ensue.

    1. *strongly agree*   2. *agree*   3. *can't say*   4. *disagree*
    5. *strongly disagree*

12. To what extent are you as a scientist involved in the normal activities of a citizen (such as regular voting, an occasional letter to an editor, etc.)?

    1. *a great deal*   2. *some*   3. *very little*   4. *none*
    5. *can't say*

13. The attitude of the scientist toward nonscientific matters (social affairs, religion, etc.) is not only different but more reliable than that of the average man.

    1. *strongly agree*   2. *agree*   3. *can't say*   4. *disagree*
    5. *strongly disagree*

14. Largely because the institutions of science and government in the United States have, through interactions, evolved into a workable system of checks and balances, we have a very strong scientific and technological community.

    1. *strongly agree*   2. *agree*   3. *can't say*   4. *disagree*
    5. *strongly disagree*

15. Science derives its political importance from the fact that it has become an integral part of a process by which accepted theories about the nature of the world — including theories used by the decision maker — are created.

    1. *strongly agree*   2. *agree*   3. *can't say*   4. *disagree*
    5. *strongly disagree*

16. The advent of science, together with specialization and the increase of technical knowledge in almost every domain, changes the conditions under which the ideal of a democratic society can be pursued — especially the belief that citizens are knowledgeable enough to control their leaders.

    1. *strongly agree*   2. *agree*   3. *can't say*   4. *disagree*
    5. *strongly disagree*

17. The federal government should directly supervise the activities of science so that its achievements are directed to socially beneficial ends.

    1. *strongly agree*   2. *agree*   3. *can't say*   4. *disagree*
    5. *strongly disagree*

18. To what degree do the following factors contribute to a scientist's ability to secure offers (of jobs, recognition, etc.) from other universities or research laboratories? (Check one for each item.)

	great deal	some	very little	none	can't say
a. school at which doctorate was taken					
b. volume of publication					
c. quality of publication					
d. teaching ability					
e. luck or chance					
f. having the right connections					

g. school or lab of 1st full-time employ

h. textbook authorship

i. self-promotion ("brass")

j. ability to get research support

19. How many scientists do you feel play an active advisory role in the making of national science policy?

   1. *less than 200*   2. *300–600*   3. *700–1000*
   4. *more than 1000*

20. Which publication represents the nearest thing there is to a spokesman for the scientific community as a whole?

   1. *Science*   2. *Bulletin of Atomic Scientists*
   3. *Scientific American*   4. *other*

21. Only those scientists who have high standing, or who work or associate informally with those who do, have the kind of information that lies at the cutting edge of inquiry.

   1. *strongly agree*   2. *agree*   3. *can't say*   4. *disagree*
   5. *strongly disagree*

22. The acceptance or nonacceptance of scientific evidence does not in any way depend upon the social position of the one who submits it (that is, his institutional affiliation [university or lab], his degree of recognition, those under whom he has studied or worked).

   1. *strongly agree*   2. *agree*   3. *can't say*   4. *disagree*
   5. *strongly disagree*

23. Scientific knowledge is not the only valid form of knowledge.

   1. *strongly agree*   2. *agree*   3. *can't say*   4. *disagree*
   5. *strongly disagree*

24. Intense personal commitment to ideas or theories is not a proper scientific attitude.

   1. *strongly agree*   2. *agree*   3. *can't say*   4. *disagree*
   5. *strongly disagree*

25. Scientists must adhere to a common set of objective standards by which proof can be demonstrated.

    1. *strongly agree*   2. *agree*   3. *can't say*   4. *disagree*
    5. *strongly disagree*

26. Most people do not understand what science is about but they accept its authority because they can see its frequent demonstration of power (bombs, rockets to the moon, new medical techniques, etc.).

    1. *strongly agree*   2. *agree*   3. *can't say*   4. *disagree*
    5. *strongly disagree*

27. The scientific method (usually thought to be a three-stage succession of hypothesis-experiment-interpretation) *generally* describes the route along which new scientific knowledge is gained.

    1. *strongly agree*   2. *agree*   3. *can't say*   4. *disagree*
    5. *strongly disagree*

28. Scientists, as a group, should make a special effort to simplify technical information for the average man.

    1. *strongly agree*   2. *agree*   3. *can't say*   4. *disagree*
    5. *strongly disagree*

29. Despite different cultural backgrounds and different patterns of belief, scientists (all over the world) can communicate effectively with each other because the terms used for communication have precisely the same meaning to the various members of the scientific community.

    1. *strongly agree*   2. *agree*   3. *can't say*   4. *disagree*
    5. *strongly disagree*

30. In the area of fundamental research, scientists regard their ideas as common property; they regard suppression of information or scientific discoveries (providing, say, national security is not threatened) as unethical.

    1. *strongly agree*   2. *agree*   3. *can't say*   4. *disagree*
    5. *strongly disagree*

31. Science differs from other professions (medicine, law, etc.) in

that there is less chance that a scientist would take advantage (financial or otherwise) of the layman.

1. *strongly agree* 2. *agree* 3. *can't say* 4. *disagree*
5. *strongly disagree*

32. Scientists are skeptical even about their own findings until other scientists have evaluated them.

1. *strongly agree* 2. *agree* 3. *can't say* 4. *disagree*
5. *strongly disagree*

33. There is a feeling today that perhaps the public record of science tends to produce a mythical imagery of scientific work. Do you feel that way? What do you feel the most important motives of scientists to be?

Appendix C

Figures

Figure C.1   AGREEMENT AND DISAGREEMENT ON UNIVERSALISM, BY INSTITUTION[a]

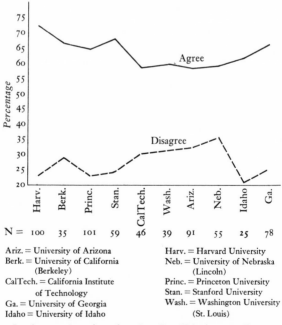

[a] Question 25 used as referent for universalism: "Scientists must adhere to a common set of objective standards by which proof can be demonstrated."

Figure C.2   AGREEMENT AND DISAGREEMENT ON UNIVERSALISM,
BY INSTITUTION[a]

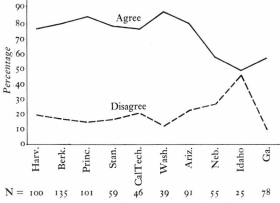

[a] Question 29 used as referent for universalism: "Despite different cultural
backgrounds and different patterns of belief, scientists (all over the world)
can communicate effectively with each other because the terms used for
communication have precisely the same meaning to the various members
of the scientific community."

Figure C.3   AGREEMENT AND DISAGREEMENT ON UNIVERSALISM,
BY INSTITUTION[a]

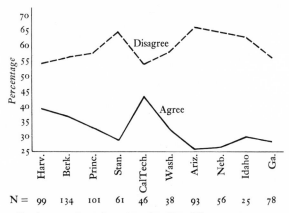

[a] Question 22 used as referent for universalism: "The acceptance or non-
acceptance of scientific evidence does not in any way depend upon the
social position of the one who submits it (that is, his institutional affiliation
[university or lab], his degree of recognition, those under whom he has
studied or worked)."

Figure C.4 AGREEMENT AND DISAGREEMENT ON UNIVERSALISM, BY DISCIPLINE[a]

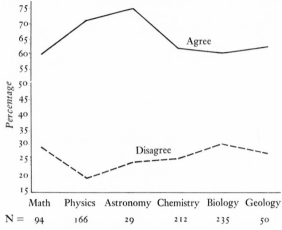

N = 94   166   29   212   235   50

[a] Question 25 used as referent for universalism: "Scientists must adhere to a common set of objective standards by which proof can be demonstrated."

Figure C.5 AGREEMENT AND DISAGREEMENT ON UNIVERSALISM, BY DISCIPLINE[a]

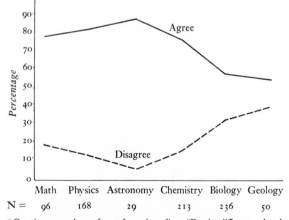

N = 96   168   29   213   236   50

[a] Question 29 used as referent for universalism: "Despite different cultural backgrounds and different patterns of belief, scientists (all over the world) can communicate effectively with each other because the terms used for communication have precisely the same meaning to the various members of the scientific community."

Figure C.6 Agreement and Disagreement on Universalism, by Discipline[a]

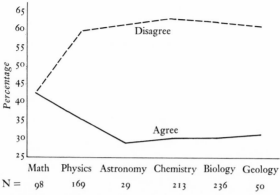

[a] Question 22 used as referent for universalism: "The acceptance or non-acceptance of scientific evidence does not in any way depend upon the social position of the one who submits it (that is, his institutional affiliation [university or lab], his degree of recognition, those under whom he has studied or worked)."

Figure C.7 Agreement and Disagreement on Universalism, by Age[a]

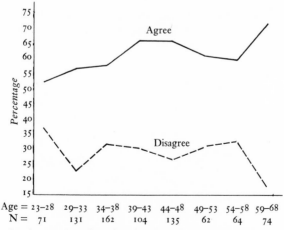

[a] Question 25 used as referent for universalism: "Scientists must adhere to a common set of objective standards by which proof can be demonstrated."

Figure C.8 AGREEMENT AND DISAGREEMENT ON UNIVERSALISM,
BY AGE[a]

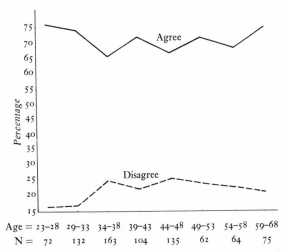

Age = 23–28 29–33 34–38 39–43 44–48 49–53 54–58 59–68
N =   72   132   163   104   135   62   64   75

[a] Question 29 used as referent for universalism: "Despite different cultural backgrounds and different patterns of belief, scientists (all over the world) can communicate effectively with each other because the terms used for communication have precisely the same meaning to the various members of the scientific community."

Figure C.9 AGREEMENT AND DISAGREEMENT ON UNIVERSALISM,
BY AGE[a]

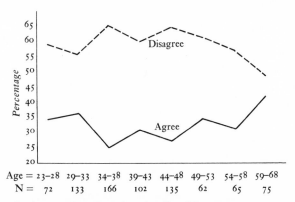

Age = 23–28 29–33 34–38 39–43 44–48 49–53 54–58 59–68
N =   72   133   166   102   135   62   65   75

[a] Question 22 used as referent for universalism: "The acceptance or non-acceptance of scientific evidence does not in any way depend upon the social position of the one who submits it (that is, his institutional affiliation [university or lab], his degree of recognition, those under whom he has studied or worked)."

Figure C.10   AGREEMENT AND DISAGREEMENT ON UNIVERSALISM,
BY "OCCUPATION"ᵃ

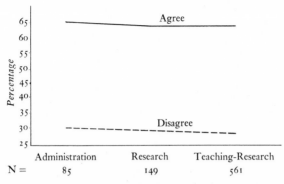

ᵃ Question 25 used as referent for universalism: "Scientists must adhere to a common set of objective standards by which proof can be demonstrated."

Figure C.11   AGREEMENT AND DISAGREEMENT ON UNIVERSALISM,
BY "OCCUPATION"ᵃ

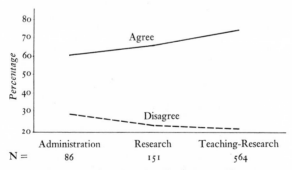

ᵃ Question 29 used as referent for universalism: "Despite different cultural backgrounds and different patterns of belief, scientists (all over the world) can communicate effectively with each other because the terms used for communication have precisely the same meaning to the various members of the scientific community."

Figure C.12 AGREEMENT AND DISAGREEMENT ON UNIVERSALISM, BY "OCCUPATION"[a]

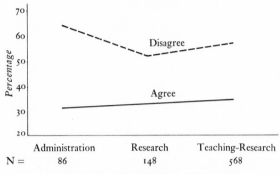

	Administration	Research	Teaching-Research
N =	86	148	568

[a] Question 22 used as referent for universalism: "The acceptance or non-acceptance of scientific evidence does not in any way depend upon the social position of the one who submits it (that his, his institutional affiliation [university or lab], his degree of recognition, those under whom he has studied or worked)."

Figure C.13 AGREEMENT AND DISAGREEMENT ON ORGANIZED SKEPTICISM, BY INSTITUTION[a]

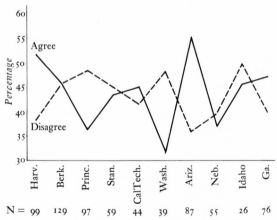

	Harv.	Berk.	Princ.	Stan.	CalTech.	Wash.	Ariz.	Neb.	Idaho	Ga.
N =	99	129	97	59	44	39	87	55	26	76

[a] Question 32 used as referent for organized skepticism: "Scientists are skeptical even about their own findings until other scientists have evaluated them."

Figure C.14 AGREEMENT AND DISAGREEMENT ON EMOTIONAL NEUTRALITY, BY INSTITUTION[a]

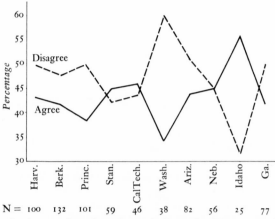

[a] Question 24 used as referent for emotional neutrality: "Intense personal commitment to ideas or theories is not a proper scientific attitude."

Figure C.15 AGREEMENT AND DISAGREEMENT ON ORGANIZED SKEPTICISM, BY DISCIPLINE[a]

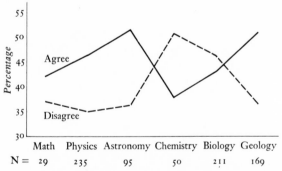

[a] Question 32 used as referent for organized skepticism: "Scientists are skeptical even about their own findings until other scientists have evaluated them."

Figure C.16 AGREEMENT AND DISAGREEMENT ON EMOTIONAL
NEUTRALITY, BY DISCIPLINE[a]

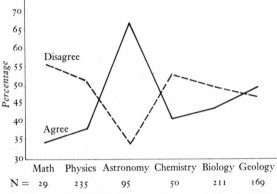

a Question 24 used as referent for emotional neutrality: "Intense personal
commitment to ideas or theories is not a proper scientific attitude."

Figure C.17 AGREEMENT AND DISAGREEMENT ON ORGANIZED
SKEPTICISM, BY AGE[a]

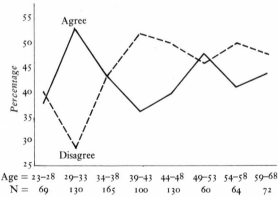

a Question 32 used as referent for organized skepticism: "Scientists are
skeptical even about their own findings until other scientists have evaluated
them."

Figure C.18   AGREEMENT AND DISAGREEMENT ON EMOTIONAL
NEUTRALITY, BY AGE[a]

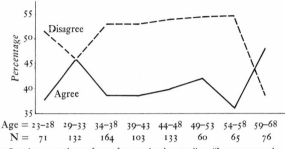

^a Question 24 used as referent for emotional neutrality: "Intense personal
commitment to ideas or theories is not a proper scientific attitude."

Figure C.19   AGREEMENT AND DISAGREEMENT ON ORGANIZED
SKEPTICISM, BY "OCCUPATION"[a]

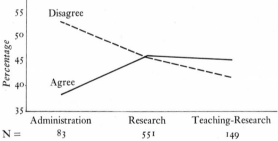

^a Question 32 used as referent for organized skepticism: "Scientists are
skeptical even about their own findings until other scientists have evaluated
them."

Figure C.20 AGREEMENT AND DISAGREEMENT ON EMOTIONAL NEUTRALITY, BY "OCCUPATION"[a]

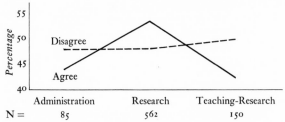

[a] Question 24 used as referent for emotional neutrality: "Intense personal commitment to ideas or theories is not a proper scientific attitude."

Index